THE TRADEMARK OF GOD

THE TRADEMARK OF GOD

*A Christian Course in
Creation, Evolution, and Salvation*

GEORGE L. MURPHY

MOREHOUSE-BARLOW
Wilton, Conn.

Morehouse-Barlow Co., Inc.
78 Danbury Road
Wilton, Connecticut 06897

Library of Congress Cataloging-in-Publication Data

Murphy, George L., 1942-
The trademark of God.

Bibliography: p.
Includes index.
1. Creation. 2. Creationism. 3. Evolution—Religious
aspects—Christianity. 4. Salvation. I. Title.
BT695.M87   1986   231.7'65   86-5402
ISBN 0-8192-1382-9

Printed in the United States of America

2 4 6 8 10 9 7 5 3 1

Contents

Acknowledgments   *vii*

Introduction   *ix*

1. The Creator of Evolution   *7*

2. God's Trademark   *8*

3. "In the Beginning . . ."   *16*

4. The Redeemer Is the Creator   *24*

5. "When the Morning Stars Sang Together"   *33*

6. Dust That Dreams   *41*

7. The Battle of the Century   *49*

8. A Chapter about Nothing   *57*

9. What Has Not Been Assumed Has
Not Been Redeemed   *65*

10. "The Dust of Death"   *73*

11. Evolutionary Ethics   *81*

12. "Unto the Ages of Ages"   *89*

Leader's Guide   *99*

*An Annotated Bibliography for the
Creation-Evolution-Christology Complex*   *129*

Index   *137*

Acknowledgments

This book is intended to help adult Christians see how Christian theology and modern science, particularly the theory of evolution, can help to inform one another. Many people and institutions have helped me in coming to the understanding which I have expressed here. Thanks are due to many students and teachers at Wartburg Seminary, and especially to Professors Norma Everist and Duane Priebe for their encouragement and advice on the thesis project in which I developed this course of study. I also appreciate the opportunity which I had at St. Andrew's Lutheran Church in Ames, Iowa, to teach a class on "Evolution and the Cosmic Christ" under the auspices of the Lay Theological Institute of Ames.

Most scriptural citations are taken from the Revised Standard Version. Citations from other published versions are noted. In a few places (Heb. 2:17 in chapter 1, Gen. 1:26 and 27 in chapters 3 and 7 and Rom. 5:12 in chapter 8) I have used my own renderings because it seemed especially important there to use inclusive language. A similar procedure was used with the citation from Article XIX of the Augsburg Confession in chapter 8, which follows Tappert's *The Book of Concord* (Philadelphia: Muhlenberg, 1959) except for the inclusive language. The quotation from Lemaître in chapter 5 is taken from Gamow's *The Creation of the Universe* (New York: Mentor, 1957).

G.L.M.

Introduction

During the past five centuries there have been a number of scientific revolutions associated with names such as Copernicus, Darwin, or Einstein. Each revolution has brought about major changes in the way humanity sees itself and the universe. The most obvious effect of these revolutions has, of course, been on the natural sciences themselves, but changes in our way of viewing the world do not affect only scientific specialists. Christian theologians, who believe that God created the universe as something "very good," and that the Word of God is irrevocably committed to the universe in the Incarnation, must take changes in scientific understanding quite seriously.

Of course, some caution is needed. Scientific theories present us with models which will probably have to be modified in important ways as science progresses. Theologians have learned painfully that the Church should not become too attached to any given scientific model. Much of the unpleasantness between science and theology has come about because some theologians could not free themselves of the Aristotelian understanding of the world that prevailed during the Middle Ages.

The Christian faith makes absolute claims, but that faith is not identical with any theology which attempts to understand and interpret it. Theology bears a relationship to the objects of faith somewhat like that which scientific theories bear to the universe that they attempt to model. Both science and theology are practices of model building. It is when we begin to think that we can simply identify our models with reality that we run into trouble.

If God's revelation comes through created means, theological and scientific understandings must interact. Our understanding of the universe will color our understanding of what God is doing in and through that universe. Thus scientific revolutions should be accompanied by at least some theological reflection. But this should not be a one-way process, for scientific understanding should not take place in complete isolation from religious belief. The Judaeo-Christian tradition was one of the major factors in the rise of modern science, and it was no accident that science developed in the Christian culture of Western Europe. It is reasonable to expect that a Christian understanding of reality may still provide some guidance for science. This will not come about through discredited procedures such as searching the Bible for hidden scientific truths or arguing for the superiority of science done by Christians. There is no special "Christian" natural science. But Christianity may help to "make sense of the sense" discovered by science. (Steven Weinberg, in his excellent book *The First Three Minutes,* describes the fantastic degree of understanding of the beginning of the universe that science has achieved, but then has to conclude that the whole thing seems "pointless." Science *by itself* finds it hard to avoid such a conclusion.)

The purpose of the present book is to help the Church to deal with the modern evolutionary view of the world, and to help Christians to use the resources of Christian theology to inform their understanding of the world. The Darwinian revolution represented a major watershed in biology, and in thought about human nature in particular. Because it touches so deeply on the questions of God's purpose and of what it means to be human, Darwinian evolution and its "neo-Darwinian" offshoots have evoked theological responses which do not yet show any sign of dying down. Yet it seems to me that the Church has not yet really addressed evolution in an adequate way.

We will not deal at great length with theological responses which simply deny evolution. Of course, evolutionary theory does need ongoing criticism, but a theology which rejects evolution is not able to come to grips with the world as we understand it today, and also does not do justice to the richness of the biblical tradition.

An approach more promising at first glance is that in which effort is directed toward "reconciling" biblical creation accounts and scientific evidence. This can be done in different ways. While such efforts may be a necessary preliminary to further theological work, they *are* preliminary, and do not really involve any deep interaction between Christian theology and science. To decide, for example, that the Hebrew word translated "day" in Genesis 1 might mean something like "geological age" rather than a twenty-four-hour day really does nothing to inform either science or theology.

What is called for is a fully Christian approach to the issues of creation and evolution. It is fundamental to Christian faith, and not merely to one or another of its theological models, that the Redeemer of the world is also its Creator. "The renewal of creation," said St. Athanasius, "has been the work of the selfsame Word that made it at the beginning."* It is only if Christ the Word is central to our understanding—central as the crucified and risen God Incarnate—that we can expect to bring the best of Christian thought to bear upon the problems which face us. We should proceed in the spirit of Martin Luther's "theology of the cross." The approach to be taken here could be called "chiasmic cosmology," for Christ's presence in the cosmos is "cross-shaped" (like the Greek letter "chi," X).

It would be wrong to suggest that no worthwhile attempts have been made before this to deal with evolution in a way that keeps Christ at the center. The work of Teilhard de Chardin is well known, and I am indebted to his important contributions. At the same time, his work has the limitations of that of almost any

---

*Athanasius, *On the Incarnation* in *Christology of the Later Fathers*, edited by Edward R. Hardy (Philadelphia: Westminster, 1954), p. 56.

pioneer. It would not be unfair to compare Teilhard's work with that of Copernicus, whose idea that the earth moved around the sun was profoundly correct, but whose system contained errors of detail.

My major concern here has been to provide adult education material for people interested in a Christian understanding of creation and evolution. While I have not attempted to include all the latest scientific developments, I have tried to present an accurate picture of the modern scientific view of the world. We all operate, perhaps unconsciously, in an atmosphere permeated by that view, and evolution plays an important role in it. Laypeople should be prepared to grapple with the implications of science for faith and faith for science. The issues with which we are concerned are too important to be left only to professional scientists and theologians.

Besides providing basic material for reading and study, the book also contains a Leader's Guide for those teaching classes or leading discussion groups with suggested readings which may be helpful. There is also an annotated bibliography for those who may be prepared to dig more deeply into some of the theological and scientific questions presented in the text.

THE TRADEMARK OF GOD

CHAPTER ONE

The Creator of Evolution

"WE BELIEVE IN ONE GOD, the Father, the Almighty, maker of heaven and earth, of all that is, seen and unseen." The Nicene Creed, the basic statement of faith of the Christian church, begins with our confession that God is the creator of the entire universe. But then we have to ask two questions. What is this universe which is created? And, more importantly, *who* is the God who made it? Exploring answers to these questions will be our task during the rest of this course. In this first chapter we'll try to get a brief overview of the most important issues which we'll be dealing with.

During the past four centuries, science has continually been expanding our picture of the universe. Our giant telescopes can now peer billions of light-years out into space, and that means billions of years back in *time*. They catch faint light signals which began their journeys long before the earth had been formed. Our radio telescopes catch the whispers left over from the "Big Bang," the cosmic explosion in which we now think the universe was formed. (That faint static may cause some of the "snow" on your TV set!) Three hundred years ago the great scientist and Christian mystic Blaise Pascal wrote, "The eternal silence of those infinite spaces strikes me with terror." And how much farther apart the stars seem to be now. . . .

Even if we stay at home on earth we can dig up fossils which

1

bring us information from the distant past of our planet. These ancient rocks which contain fossilized plants and animals are like time capsules which have been buried for many millions of years in the earth's crust. We learn from them about the forms of life which existed in earth's remote past, plants and animals which today are nowhere to be seen. And the thought may occur to us—maybe dogs and cats and redwood trees and human beings are not any more permanent than those vanished species were.

The story which all of the scientific evidence combines to tell us is mind-blowing. The universe is gigantic beyond our ability to imagine. It may be infinite in extent. And it's a universe which is always in the process of change—of becoming. The whole universe is evolving, and we have no idea what forms of life it may harbor in some distant star cluster or in the future of our planet. What we do know is that everything is changing. The very continents move under our feet, a fraction of an inch each year.

The galaxies, vast swarms of hundreds of billions of stars which are each as huge as our sun, fly apart from one another as the universe expands. New stars are born from immense gas clouds, go through their life cycles measured in millions or billions of years, and die explosive or quiet deaths. In the course of their evolution, these stars may give rise to families of planets like our solar system. Mountains rise and fall on the surface of a planet, seas form, and complex chemicals in those seas group together to form the first microscopic living organisms.

New living species are formed from older ones, grow, adapt to new environments—or perhaps become extinct. For the environment will favor the survival of some species more than it will of others, and the favored species will be more likely to survive to produce offspring. Advantageous variations will be preserved and slowly accumulate, and organisms will gradually change their characteristics as the generations pass. The simple one-celled organisms of three billion years ago have been transformed by such processes of small, random variations to produce the astonishing variety of living creatures which we see around us today.

Where is God in all of this? "Nowhere!" some people have

answered triumphantly. "Maybe the whole universe began itself somehow—or perhaps it's existed forever. Maybe there did have to be some sort of God to get things started. But in any case, that was all in the past. The universe seems to be able to take care of itself pretty well now. We've been able to discover many of the rules by which the universe seems to run—what we call the laws of nature—and these laws don't involve God in any way. If God exists, he leaves the universe alone. We've long since gotten away from the idea that some God sends disease or lightning to punish sins, or that miracles are worked for those who are especially good.

"There's simply no need to suppose that God created a perfect universe in the beginning," they will go on, "and no evidence for it. Certainly the idea that we descended from a single couple like Adam and Eve doesn't agree with the evidence which we now have about primitive human beings. We're here because our ancestors were better fitted than their competitors in the struggle for survival. Maybe we'd like to think that we're more special than that, that 'somebody up there likes us,' but grown-ups have to learn the difference between wishes and reality."

But there are others who will respond quite differently to the challenge of new discoveries. Some Christians want to deal with the attacks on the Faith which science seems to produce by denying the immense age of the universe, and especially by denying that biological evolution has taken place. "Christians have to depend on what God has told us in scripture, not on fallible human reason," they may argue. "Evolution could never be more than a theory, since there were no people to observe how God made the world. Therefore we have to trust God's word. You really have only two choices. Either believe that God made the whole universe, including men and women, in the beginning, just as the Genesis account teaches, or accept evolution. But if you do that, be honest enough to admit that you're an atheist."

And so the struggle has gone on for a century and a quarter since Charles Darwin published his *The Origin of Species*. During this time, extreme views like those which we've outlined have tended to grab most of the headlines. It's true that these *are* extreme views. Few scientists go out of their way to attack religion, and many Christians have concluded that it's quite possible for them to believe that evolution is the process which God used in the creation of species. In fact, there are many Christians actively working in some of these areas at the frontiers of science.

But the debate does go on. It has been especially heated in recent years over the issue of whether evolution or "creationism"— or both, or neither—should be taught in the public schools. That's a question which strikes especially close to home for Americans, for the public schools play a very important role in our whole picture of what society ought to be. And so we can't expect the controversy over evolution and creation simply to disappear.

This all makes us wonder if there might not be some important point which we're missing. (That often turns out to be the case when people keep going around and around an issue without getting anywhere.) And in fact, we ought to get a little suspicious when we realize that very little of the discussion about creation and evolution ever has much to do with the central concerns of the Christian faith. The creation accounts of Genesis are important, but they are not the things which distinguish us as *Christians*. (Jews and Muslims accept them too.) What does Jesus Christ have to do with any of this?

For "the Father, the Almighty, maker of heaven and earth" is not primarily some cosmic watchmaker who wound up the universe and started it ticking in the beginning before going into retirement. Nor is God some super-philosopher, occupied in thinking somewhere beyond the clouds. God is the creator of the cosmic "machinery," and the one who "thinks the laws of nature" —but God is more.

God is the one who raised Jesus from the dead.

What things are really important to us as Christians? What are the great festivals which we celebrate together as a community, as the Body of Christ?

Christmas—the one "by whom all things were made" entered human life, "came down from heaven" and took our flesh in the womb of Mary. God took to himself the carbon and hydrogen and oxygen, the proteins and the genes of which *we* are made. The Word of God, "eternally begotten of the Father," lies as a baby in a stable in one of Bethlehem's caves, as our ancestors huddled in the caves for protection against the cold of the Ice Age. ("He had to be made like his brothers and sisters in every respect"— Heb. 2:17.) God takes the whole fallen world to himself, and so we pray to Christ as "Redeemer of the world."

Easter—God brings life out of death, something out of nothing. From the impossibility of hope in abandonment and shameful death, from the destruction of all our human hopes, God brings a new creation by raising Jesus from the grave. "For we know that Christ being raised from the dead will never die again; death no longer has dominion over him" (Rom. 6:9). It's a lot like God's creation of the universe out of nothing, the "without form and void," in the beginning. That's the trademark of all of God's creative work—creation out of nothing.

(Just as life, just as humanity, came to be through the "struggle" for survival, through pain and death, through extinction. The trademark of God. . . .)

"In the beginning God created the heavens and the earth."

"The universe is dynamic and evolving."

Both of these statements are true. The first is a statement of faith, coming from God's revelation in Holy Scripture. The second is a statement which we have read, with considerable toil and with many wrong turns and blind alleys, in the "Book of Nature" which God has placed before us. In order to make the first statement, we have to be open to trust in God as the creator. In order to make the second statement, we have to be willing to use the brains and the skills which God has given to us. For the Christian, these two statements reinforce one another.

And it is Christ who ties these two statements together, who makes it possible for us to understand something about the religious significance of evolution *and* about the importance of evolution for the meaning of our faith. Christ is the Lord of the entire universe, and we look to him to give meaning to all of life.

"He exists before everything, and all things are held together in him" (Col. 1:17, NEB).

Let's stop for a moment to catch our breath. We've gone very quickly, and have taken a hurried look at a lot of important ideas. The Christian doctrine of creation, the modern scientific picture of the universe and of the evolution of life, and the significance of the person and work of Christ are the three major themes which were emphasized. They have been dealt with in a very condensed way in this introductory chapter just so we'll know what we'll be exploring. The purpose of the following pages is to help in unpacking those themes and to see how they are related to one another. Along the way, we want to try to understand why the issue of creation and evolution has raised so many problems. We'll also explore some of the implications which these topics have for the way we deal with life in our world today. Here are some of the things we'll be thinking about.

The biblical doctrine of creation. What do the Old and the New Testaments say about God's creative work? The first chapters of Genesis are very important here but, as we'll see, they aren't the whole story.

The scientific picture of the universe. Science has shaped our views perhaps more than we realize, and we need to examine a few of its basic ideas with some care. What does it mean for us to talk about a changing universe? Why do scientists seem so certain about evolution? And what does evolutionary theory really say about human beings?

Trouble spots. Theology and science, if we understand them properly, should not really be in conflict. There will, however, be some areas in which, in their growth, they will seem to rub together rather painfully, and we want to look at some of these.

The mystery of evil. And evil always has to remain something of a mystery. But it has to be faced. How are we to think of the existence of evil in God's creation? And what connection can there be between the Christian teaching that we are "fallen" human beings and the idea that we have evolved from "lower" forms of life?

Christ the center. Jesus is not just the savior of human beings but of the whole world. We will examine the church's ancient teachings about the person and work of Christ in order to see how they illuminate what science has uncovered about our relationship with the rest of the world. And we will try to see how the universe looks from the standpoint of the cross.

And—*What difference does it all make?* Creation and Christ and evolution are literally life and death matters, not just subjects for scholarly arguments. They are as relevant as the issues which concern us every day of our lives—education, war, the environment, abortion, and the relationship between men and women. In fact, the topics which we'll be studying here are not just some items to be placed alongside those others on our list of concerns. Studying our relationship with one another and with the whole of creation in Jesus Christ will give us some help in our thinking about those other issues.

We'll begin in what seems to be the middle of the Old Testament, with the stories of the Exodus and of God bringing his people back from exile in Babylon. This is where biblical thinking about God begins—with his saving work in human history. That is *creative* work, for God makes life and community where none was before. Then it will be time to look at the creation of the whole world in Genesis, and the renewal of the world in the New Testament.

And now—the whole universe which God has created and redeemed in Christ is our playground. Have fun!

CHAPTER TWO

God's Trademark

GOD CREATED HIS PEOPLE ISRAEL in the Exodus from Egypt. Israel had been enslaved there—they had been no nation, no "people" at all. Even though they remembered some things about their great ancestors, Abraham, Isaac, and Jacob, they seem to have lost the memory of the God their parents worshiped, and probably served the many gods and goddesses of their slavemasters. Loaded with heavy burdens, the lives of their sons threatened by a king who wanted to kill them, all the people could do was to cry out. And they didn't even know to whom they should cry!

Israel was at rock bottom. Israel was nothing at all.

> And the people of Israel groaned under their bondage, and cried out for help, and their cry under bondage came up to God. And God heard their groaning, and God remembered his covenant with Abraham, with Isaac, and with Jacob. (Ex. 2:23-24)

Humanly speaking, God has nothing to work with. There is nothing that looks like promising material in Egypt, nothing with the potential to become God's people. But God acts, calling Moses from the midst of the bush that burned yet was not burned up. Through Moses, God led the people out of Egypt, bringing them through the Red Sea, but destroying their oppressors in the waters.

This is the first great act of creation that God's people knew.

They had to be brought out of bondage before they could know of the Lord as the creator of all nations, and of the whole world. And the memory of the Exodus colored the way that Israel thought of all God's work. It is remembered, and sung, and confessed, time after time in the Old Testament. One of the oldest verses in our Bible may be the Song of Miriam, the song in which the prophetess led the women of Israel on the other side of the sea:

> Sing to the LORD, for he has triumphed gloriously;
> the horse and his rider he has thrown into the sea. (Ex. 15:21)

Israel's confession of faith is that God acted in human history to bring the people out of Egypt. The profession of faith in Dt. 26:5-9 is just this statement of Israel's enslavement in Egypt, and of God's salvation which is given in the Exodus:

> The LORD brought us out of Egypt with a mighty hand and
> an outstretched arm, with great terror, with signs and wonders.
> (Dt. 26:8)

The Hebrews weren't concerned, to begin with, about how God created the universe, and they didn't go in much for philosophical discussions about the origin of the world. What they did know was that they owed their lives to God's saving action.

But they also told the Exodus story in ways that proclaimed the God of the Exodus as the one who defeats all the powers of evil. For those desert-dwelling nomads, the sea was always a symbol of death and destruction. The fact that God could save them *through* the sea meant that the Lord was mightier than any evil power. Frightening mythical images of dragons and "chaos monsters" lurking in the sea no longer had to scare them. The Lord had beaten all the destructive forces which dwelt in the Deep and threatened creation:

> Thou didst divide the sea by thy might;
> thou didst break the heads of the dragons on the waters.
> (Ps. 74:13)

God makes himself known in history by his actions. *God is the Lord, who created Israel out of nothing in the Exodus.*

Israel was called to be faithful to the Lord, in response to his loving act of creation. Obedience to the laws which God gives is to be in acknowledgment of the fact that God has made us:

> You have seen what I did to the Egyptians, and how I bore you on eagles' wings and brought you to myself. Now therefore, if you will obey my voice and keep my covenant, you shall be my own possession among all peoples; for all the earth is mine. (Ex. 19:4-5)

But Israel soon began to want to be like all the nations around them, and to trust in foreign gods. They wanted to be an empire, and to have military power and wealth and security that they could rely on. (Trusting in God as your creator means trusting each day that your life, and all that you need for life, will be given to you. It means not trying to hoard up what you need so that you can rely on yourself. That's why we pray, "Give us this day our daily bread.") So Israel depended on its horses and chariots, like the Egyptians whom God had thrown into the waters of chaos.

Israel turned to others for its life, to Canaanite gods and goddesses of fertility like Baal or Asherah. The yearly "rebirth" of vegetation and the reproductive power of sex were the most important aspects of creation, and by turning to these deities, Israel was turning away from the Lord as its creator. So God complains of Israel,

> She did not know that I gave her corn, and wine, and oil, and multiplied her silver and gold, which they prepared for Baal. (Hos. 2:8, KJV)

And the heavenly powers could not be neglected—it took no giant telescopes or astrology magazines for the people of antiquity to be in awe of the stars and planets. These celestial beings might have tremendous power over human life! So King Manasseh of Judah "built altars for all the host of heaven in the two courts of the house of the LORD" (2 Kg. 21:5).

Israel no longer really believed that the Lord created and saved and sustained them. And because of their unfaithfulness, because of their unwillingness to trust in the one who had made them a people in the Exodus, Israel was dispersed and carried off into exile. The Babylonians burned the Holy City and the House of God to the ground, put the rulers to death, and carried all the people of importance into exile.

(Does that horrible wish for Babylon in Psalm 137—"Happy shall he be who takes your little ones and dashes them against the rock!"—carry some memory of what the Israelites had seen Babylonian troops do in the courts of the Temple?)

The Lord's people have been destroyed, returned to chaos and nothingness. The nation no longer exists, and no longer has any human hope of existing. God himself has been defeated—for if a god can't save his people, what good is he?

"Our God has been beaten," the exiles might have said. "The Lord is inferior to the gods and goddesses of Babylon, to Bel and Marduk, Ishtar and Nebo who gave Babylon the empire of the world. Maybe we should serve them, and participate in the great New Year's celebration, when the glorious images of the gods are carried in procession through the streets. And we'll hear the great creation epic telling of how the gods made the world in the beginning, how they created men and women as slaves of the gods, and set the stars and planets over us."

In the middle of all this darkness, God raised up one of the greatest of the prophets—but one whose name we don't even know! We call him the Second Isaiah because his writings now form the fortieth through the fifty-fifth chapters of the Book of Isaiah. Those chapters really need to be read in their entirety, for quoting a few excerpts from them hardly does justice to this great hymn of the promise of life from the creator of the universe.

God proclaims to these hopeless and emptied exiles that he is still the Lord who created Israel through the waters of death:

But now thus says the LORD,
he who created you, O Jacob,

he who formed you, O Israel:
"Fear not, for I have redeemed you;
I have called you by name, you are mine.
When you pass through the waters I will be with you;
and through the rivers, they shall not overwhelm you;
when you walk through fire you shall not be burned,
and the flame shall not consume you.
For I am the LORD your God, the Holy One of Israel, your
    Savior."   (Is. 43:1-3a)

But the Lord did not create only Israel, the prophet declares.
He made the whole universe—Israel and Babylon, heaven and
earth.

Have you not known? Have you not heard?
Has it not been told you from the beginning?
Have you not understood from the foundations of the earth?
It is he who sits above the circle of the earth,
and its inhabitants are like grasshoppers;
who stretches out the heavens like a curtain,
and spreads them like a tent to dwell in;

    . . . . . .

To whom then will you compare me, that I should be like him?
    says the Holy One.
Lift up your eyes on high and see: who created these?
He who brings out their host by number,
calling them all by name;
by the greatness of his might,
and because he is strong in power not one is missing.

    . . . . . .

Have you not known? Have you not heard?
The LORD is the everlasting God, the Creator of the ends of
    the earth.   (Is. 40:21-22, 25-26, 28a)

How can these Babylonian idols, who have to be carried around
by people and animals in processions, carry anyone? How can they
bear the weight of the universe?

Bel bows down, Nebo stoops,

their idols are on beasts and cattle;
these things you carry are loaded as burdens on weary beasts.
They stoop, they bow down together,
they cannot save the burden,
but themselves go into captivity.
"Hearken to me, O house of Jacob,
all the remnant of the house of Israel,
who have been borne by me from your birth,
carried from the womb;
even to your old age I am He,
and to gray hairs I will carry you.
I have made, and I will bear;
I will carry and will save."   (Is. 46:1-4)

But "He is not the God of the dead, but of the living." The
exiles aren't just called to listen to a history lesson or to a story
about long ago, in a galaxy far, far away. The creator of Israel,
the creator of the universe, is doing something *new*—for creation
out of nothing always means newness. God will bring the scattered
Israelites back from the nothingness of exile. God will again create
life out of death.

"I am the LORD, your Holy One,
the Creator of Israel, your King."
Thus says the LORD,
who makes a way in the sea,
a path in the mighty waters,
who brings forth chariot and horse, army and warrior;
they lie down, they cannot rise,
they are extinguished, quenched like a wick:
"Remember not the former things,
nor consider the things of old.
Behold, I am doing a new thing;
now it springs forth, do you not perceive it?
I will make a way in the wilderness
and rivers in the desert.
The wild beasts will honor me,
the jackals and the ostriches;
for I give water in the wilderness,

rivers in the desert,
to give drink to my chosen people,
the people whom I formed for myself
that they might declare my praise."   (Is. 43:15-21)

In the new Exodus, God will bring Israel through the desert into the land of promise, and will again make them the people of God. All of the idols, all of the powers of darkness and chaos, are broken by God—by God's Word:

For as the rain and the snow come down from heaven,
and return not thither but water the earth,
making it bring forth and sprout,
giving seed to the sower and bread to the eater,
so shall my word be that goes forth from my mouth;
it shall not return to me empty,
but it shall accomplish that which I purpose,
and prosper in the thing for which I sent it.   (Is. 55:10-11)

And God does bring Israel back. They are a tiny and weak people, still with evil and dangers around them, but now they have a new vision. The God of Israel is the Lord of the whole world, "maker of heaven and earth." "For all the gods of the nations are idols: but the LORD made the heavens" (Ps. 96:5, KJV).

The Lord who brought Israel out of Egypt is the God who made the universe from nothing in the beginning.

God, who created the universe and acted in human history, is still active. God is still working, still bringing "something from nothing" in his saving acts. That is why Scripture speaks of the Lord as "the living God," and taunts the heathen idols who are unable to *do* anything.

Creation out of nothing is God's trademark. It is the sign which authenticates all of God's work.

When we look at the stories of the Old Testament in the light of this idea, with what we have seen of the Exodus and the return from exile, we find many more places in which this mark is prominent. God carried Noah and his family through the flood waters which destroyed the old world, and brought from them new life. God gave old Abraham and Sarah, who were far beyond the age to have children, the child of promise, bringing life out of the barren womb. God brings hope when all human hope is gone. ("So Sarah laughed to herself, saying, 'After I have grown old, and my husband is old, shall I have pleasure?' "—Gen. 18:12.)

The writers of the creation stories of Genesis, which we'll be considering in the next chapter, talk about what it means for the mark of God to be placed on the human race and on the whole universe. While the Jews, like all intelligent people, wondered about the structure of the universe and how it came into being, their main concern was always to acknowledge God *alone* as the source of being and life. So a Jewish mother encouraged her last son to follow his brothers in martyrdom rather than give up faith in God the creator:

> I beg you, child, look at the sky and the earth; see all that is in them and realize that God made them out of nothing, and that man comes into being in the same way. Do not be afraid of this butcher; accept death and prove yourself worthy of your brothers, so that by God's mercy I may receive you back again along with them. (2 Macc. 7:28-29, NEB)

But God's people also look forward. When will the waters of death be swept away forever? There is still evil in the world, and people still die:

> The righteous perish,
> and no one takes it to heart.   (Is. 57:1 NEB)

What can God's creation out of nothing mean for those in the graves of Israel (Ez. 37:11-13), for those who lie in the dust of the earth—the dust of death? The Old Testament strains toward the hope of new creation, toward the resurrection of the dead. But we must wait. The theme of God's creation out of nothing is the theme of the passion and resurrection of Christ. The trademark of God is the sign of the cross, the sign which God places on the universe from the beginning.

We come to that in the next chapter. There was nothing— not time, nor space, nor matter. And God spoke. . . .

CHAPTER THREE

"In the Beginning . . ."

ON CHRISTMAS EVE OF 1968 the world watched and listened as the Apollo 8 astronauts rounded the moon—the first humans ever to see its far side. The very fact that we could hear their voices over a quarter of a million miles of space was a triumph of science. And there were a lot of things that those men could have said about human progress and new frontiers. Maybe a little boasting wouldn't have been out of place. Then, over that quarter of a million miles, we heard them read:

> In the beginning God created the heaven and the earth. And the earth was without form, and void; and darkness was upon the face of the deep. And the Spirit of God moved upon the face of the waters. And God said, Let there be light: and there was light. (Gen. 1:1-3, KJV)

Whatever human beings may accomplish, it is *God* who creates and sustains the universe. In the beginning there was nothing, only void and chaos, and *God* created the heavens and the earth.

The Genesis accounts of creation proclaim God's sovereignty and his care for the world and its life. They are not scientific reports or theories about the early universe. That is not at all to say that they are wrong, though they would seem to be in conflict with scientific discoveries if we were to view them as *rival* scientific theories. It's always important to know what *kind* of document you're reading. We don't read a love letter in the same way we read one from the Internal Revenue Service, and we don't read the Bible as if it were a geology textbook.

For our study of Genesis, an important first step is to realize that we have there *two* accounts of creation, showing somewhat different concerns and interests. It can be exciting to discover the richness of the biblical tradition that comes from having more than one way of viewing the work of God. (We can be thankful that we have four gospels rather than just one, though the basic story is the same in each.)

The first creation account, which goes from Genesis 1:1 through the first half of 2:4, was probably the second one to be written. It may have been put in its final form after the return from exile in Babylon, for it proclaims very clearly that the God of Israel, and not the heathen deities of the surrounding nations, is the creator. This majestic hymn of creation shows the complete control of God over the universe and over all the powers of chaos that threaten it. Creation takes place through the Word of God alone—"God said, 'Let there be light,' and there was light."

Scholars debate whether or not the original author of this creation story thought of the universe as being created out of nothing. The first verses of Genesis can be translated to suggest either that God created the world out of nothing, or that God's creative work began when the universe was in a chaotic state. The King James translation quoted earlier adopts the first choice, while the Today's English Version ("In the beginning, when God created the universe, the earth was formless and desolate") chooses the second. The biblical tradition in which the Genesis accounts are set teaches (as we saw in the previous chapter) that God does create out of nothing. And to the Old Testament writers, the difference between creation out of nothing and creation *in spite of* chaos and disordered matter is not as great as we might think. For God does not make the world *out of* chaos, as in some pagan myths the creator makes the earth and sky out of the body of some slain giant or dragon. Complete chaos means the "impossibility" of an ordered world, and God creates an ordered world in spite of that, through the Word. The "without form and void" and the "deep" of Genesis 1:2 are unable to put up any resistance to God's command.

(It's interesting also to note that modern science has come to the realization that pattern is really essential to matter. "Structure" and "substance" can't be separated, so that the idea of "formless matter" almost amounts to that of "nothingness.")

The picture of the universe assumed in Genesis is that of pre-scientific geography and astronomy. The (flat) earth floats on the "world ocean," and over it, like a dome, is the "firmament" which holds off the waters above. But when it is necessary in order to declare God's sovereignty, the accepted "common sense" views of Israel's neighbors about the world are decisively rejected. The Babylonians, among whom the Jews had lived as exiles, thought that the heavenly bodies, the sun and moon and stars, controlled events on earth. Many nations have worshiped the sun god or the moon goddess, or have thought (with those today who believe in astrology) that the stars rule their lives. So Genesis 1 delays the making of sun and moon until the *fourth* day of creation. The stars are left almost to an afterthought: "And the stars," the writer adds at the end of 1:16, putting these "deities" in their place.

So a definite theological statement is made by delaying the creation of the heavenly bodies till the fourth day, when we might have expected this to precede the creation of plant life. But even with this, there is a quite orderly sequence of creation days. Plants are created, then sea creatures and birds, land animals and, as the climax of creation, humanity. (But it doesn't work very well to try to make these days correspond to geological ages or something like that. Again, the biblical account is theological proclamation, not a scientist's observation notebook.)

The idea in this account is that God creates living creatures by commanding the seas and the earth to produce them. God doesn't say, "Let there be dinosaurs, let there be horses, etc." but "Let the earth bring forth living creatures according to their kinds . . . ." In the same way, the earth had been commanded to bring forth vegetation and the waters to bring forth sea creatures.

The inanimate waters and earth have the potential to bring forth life when activated by the divine command.

Then God takes counsel before the greatest and final work, the human race, and proclaims his intention:

> Let us make humanity in our image, after our likeness; and let them have dominion over the fish of the sea, and over the birds of the air, and over the cattle, and over all the earth, and over every creeping thing that creeps upon the earth. (Gen. 1:26)

And it was as God commanded.

> So God created humanity in his own image, in the image of God he created him; male and female he created them. (Gen. 1:27)

What does it mean for humanity to be created in the image of God? One answer is already given in verse 26: "Let them have dominion. . . ." The human race is to be God's representative in ruling creation. This means that we are to show love and care for the whole world, and should not merely exploit it for ourselves. We are made to have the same concern for the world that God has—and God's love for creation extends even to giving up himself for it.

The teachers of the early church emphasized another aspect of the image of God—that human beings are able to hear and to respond to God's Word, to think about the universe and to understand it. It is largely because we are rational creatures that we are *able* to "have dominion."

It is important to remember that, for all the rationality and dominion that humanity is given, women and men are not set up as little goddesses and gods who can operate independently of their creator. Humanity was made to hear and to respond to the Word of God, and it is only that which gives meaning to our lives. The desire to "be like God, knowing good and evil" (Gen. 3:5), to have the source of our lives within ourselves, is something quite different. That belongs to the story of humanity's sin.

At the close of the sixth day, "God saw everything that he had made, and behold, it was very good" (Gen. 1:31). Creation is good. The material universe is worth studying and trying to understand because it is the good work of God. Here, at the beginning of the Bible, is a firm rejection of all attempts to devalue the world or to suggest that we ought to be concerned only with "spiritual" matters. Six times in the first chapter of Genesis we have been told that different parts of creation were judged "good" by God. Now, at the end, the whole creation is seen by God as "very good."

And God rested on the seventh day. The Sabbath rest of the Jews acknowledged their dependence on God, for it means that a person can't sustain his or her own life by continual labor. Keeping the Sabbath means praising God by looking to him for life, and the creation story proclaims that time for this is built into God's basic design for the universe.

The second creation account begins in the middle of Genesis 2:4. Differences of style, as well as of theological focus, mark it off from the first account. For example, the creator is referred to as "the Lord God" throughout 2:4b-3:24, rather than "God" as in 1:1-2:4a. This second account may have been written around a thousand years before the time of Christ.

If the first account is a hymn which proclaims the sovereignty of God in creation, the second has more the form of a story in which God's immediate and loving care for humanity is proclaimed. Here God does not create by command, but literally gets down in the dirt in order to accomplish his purpose.

No details are given about the formation of earth and heaven. The second account begins with an earth uninhabited and barren, and God's first creative work is to make man. God *forms* "the Adam" "of dust from the ground" (Gen. 2:7), and breathes the breath of life into him. Humanity is earthly, earthy, a material creature enlivened by relationship with God.

But humanity is not complete in one person—"It is not good that the man should be alone" (Gen. 2:18). The Hebrew word *Adam* means, in fact, humanity, and not only a single male. The other animals which God creates are good, but not good enough to make the man fully what he is to be. Only woman, formed from man (and from whom man in turn comes, as 1 Corinthians 11:12 points out) completes humanity. An isolated human being is not really complete, for men and women are created to live in community. "Therefore a man leaves his father and his mother and cleaves to his wife, and they become one flesh" (Gen. 2:24). Woman is made as "a helper fit for him" (Gen. 2:18)—not an inferior servant, but an equal partner.

We see here an agreement with the collective aspect of the "image of God" in the first account, in which God says, "Let *them* have dominion. . . ." And the dominion which humanity exercises over other creatures appears here in Adam's naming of the beasts. For the Hebrews, to know the true name of a thing was to have power over it. Here, in the garden which God has planted for his creatures, the beasts submit peacefully to the rule of men and women. Humanity has insight into the nature of things, and rules the world made for it.

We are not, however, to live in idle luxury. "The LORD God took the man and put him in the garden of Eden to till it and keep it" (Gen. 2:15). To work with the material world, to keep it in order, is part of the purpose of humanity from the very beginning.

So man and woman are happy in paradise—but we have read further, and we know that the dream ends. "Now the serpent was more subtle than any other wild creature that the LORD God had made" (Gen. 3:1)—it comes like the stroke of midnight for Cinderella. And as her clothes and carriage changed back into rags and pumpkin, the story of the sin of humanity in Genesis 3 brings us back to what we know we really are: "You are dust, and to dust you shall return" (Gen. 3:19).

We will talk about this story of our sin in a later chapter, when we try to understand the presence of evil in our world. We know that the core of the story is true—that we have turned away from God, and are on the way to death. But now the pressing question about all of this is, *were* those stories of creation only a dream? What do they have to do with the real world?

The message of the Genesis creation accounts is a powerful

one. God creates and sustains the universe "by his word of power" (Heb. 1:3) against all destructive forces. Humanity is created in God's image to be God's representative in creation. Men and women, made from the dust, are the special concern and pride of God. In a world which is often seen as meaningless, and for men and women who are often treated as disposable pieces of junk, that is a message that has to be proclaimed over and over again.

On the other hand, Genesis simply is not helpful if we try to make it do something it wasn't intended to do. The layers of rock in which fossils are deposited show that the development of the plants and animals which live today took billions of years, not six literal days. If we use the genealogies of the Old Testament to work back to the date of creation, we find an age for the earth of something like six thousand years instead of the billions which scientific methods indicate. But the purpose of those genealogies is to show the connection between human history and God's creative work, not to date that work.

This is not to suggest that Genesis has nothing to say to science. The goodness of creation which Genesis speaks of is one of the basic assumptions which makes science worth doing. And in more detail, we have seen that the Genesis accounts agree in fundamental ways with what the evolutionary view of life has to say. We are "dust from the ground," and the creatures of the world have all been "brought forth" from the waters and the earth. The picture of all living creatures as an interrelated, interdependent whole is one shared by science and Christian theology.

The early teachers of the church were sometimes able to see this more clearly than we are today. One of them in particular, Gregory of Nyssa, a fourth-century theologian who was one of the major formers of our doctrine of the Trinity, came very close to teaching the evolution of humanity. He saw that Genesis taught the "bringing forth" of life from the waters and the earth, and argued that this was by virtue of powers which God had placed in these elements in the first instant of creation. Humanity, he believed, then had to pass through "vegetative" and "animal" stages before reaching the final stage of being a rational, living animal. God chose to exercise his creative power in this kind of gradual development.

We must be careful not to try to make Gregory into more than he really was. He did not develop any theory of evolution, or even state one in so many words. Yet the example of this important theologian shows that the Christian church has, from its earliest days, been prepared to interpret Genesis in a manner that agrees in basic ways with the theory of evolution. That is an important lesson for an age in which evolution is sometimes linked to a rejection of the Genesis accounts and to atheism.

To finish our look at the biblical doctrine of creation, we turn next to the New Testament. There the theme is that, in Christ, the creator of the universe has come into the world as a creature to renew his creation.

CHAPTER FOUR

The Redeemer Is the Creator

"IN THE BEGINNING," starts the Old Testament, "God created the heavens and the earth." God spoke, and the universe was made.

"In the beginning," starts the Gospel of John, "was the Word, and the Word was with God, and the Word was God. . . . All things were made through him, and without him was not anything made that was made. . . . And the Word became flesh, and dwelt among us."

We began our study of creation with the Old Testament. That is a traditional way to start, but it has its dangers. It might suggest that the idea of creation is restricted to the Old Testament, and that the New Testament deals with something quite different, redemption. In reality, there is a common theme running throughout the Bible. All the work of God described in Scripture bears God's trademark. The one who redeems is the creator, and salvation is new creation.

There is something new, though it is something that was from the beginning. The coming of the creator in human flesh, his death and resurrection, were hinted at in the Old Testament. And when we look back at the events and teachings of the time before Christ in the light of the cross, we see Scripture as a unity. The great acts of creation in the past are not God's greatest works. The Flood, the Exodus, and the return from exile are all incomplete, and strain toward something greater. Even the creation of the world in the beginning is incomplete, for God's "Sabbath rest" does not mean that the creator is no longer active. The world yearns for the greater Sabbath, when its pains and sorrows will be done away with. So Jesus heals the lame and the blind on the Sabbath, and tells his critics, "My Father is working still, and I am working" (Jn. 5:17).

God does do new things, though they bear the old trademark. God is active and on the move—the God who creates through change and evolution. The God of Israel is not, first of all, identified with a sacred *place*, with some sanctuary where worship is to be offered. He is, in fact, the God of *Israel*, the God who goes with his people. He shares their travels through the wilderness, where the sanctuary of God is a tent which can be packed up and carried along on the journey. Even when King Solomon has finally built a temple for God, a holy place, the prophets proclaim that God will abandon that place and destroy the temple if the people are unfaithful. That threat is fulfilled when they are carried off into exile in Babylon and, as we saw in chapter 2, God again created his people out of nothing.

Finally Jesus stands in the courts of the grandiose new temple which Herod has built, after cleansing it of the money-changers:

> The Jews then said to him, "What sign have you to show us for doing this?" Jesus answered them, "Destroy this temple, and in three days I will raise it up." The Jews then said, "It has taken forty-six years to build this temple, and will you raise it up in three days?" But he spoke of the temple of his body. (Jn. 2:18-21)

God has come to share the journey of his people.

For in Jesus Christ, the creator of the world is present. The New Testament writers state this quite clearly:

> All things were made through him: and without him was not anything made that was made. (Jn. 1:3)

> He is the image of the invisible God, the first-born of all

creation; for in him all things were created, in heaven and on earth, visible and invisible, whether thrones or dominions or principalities or authorities—all things were created through him and for him. He is before all things, and in him all things hold together. (Col. 1:15-17)

The presence of the creator is also made clear by the actions of Jesus, and especially from some of the miracle stories. These miracles are not arbitrary interferences with the laws of nature. Jesus refuses the suggestion that he turn stones into bread, but he will turn a *little* bread into a *lot* of bread.

One of his disciples, Andrew, Simon Peter's brother, said to him, "There is a lad here who has five barley loaves and two fish; but what are they among so many?" Jesus said, "Make the people sit down." Now there was much grass in the place; so the men sat down, in number about five thousand. Jesus then took the loaves, and when he had given thanks, he distributed them to those who were seated; so also the fish, as much as they wanted. And when they had eaten their fill, he told his disciples, "Gather up the fragments left over, that nothing may be lost." (Jn. 6:8-12)

This is the style of the one who sustains the world. Each year a little grain, scattered on the fields, becomes a lot of grain. God maintains creation through the laws of nature which describe, among other things, the growth of the grain. But once, on a hillside in Palestine, God did the same thing in a way that appears miraculous to us.

We have come to expect that grain will grow from the buried seed. That's part of the cycle of nature—but a part that symbolizes life from death and hope in hopeless situations. Jesus proclaims that as the way of life, the path that he will follow and the path that he calls his disciples to take.

And Jesus answered them, "The hour has come for the Son of man to be glorified. Truly, truly, I say to you, unless a grain of wheat falls into the earth and dies, it remains alone; but if it dies, it bears much fruit. He who loves his life loses it, and he who hates his life in this world will keep it for eternal life. If anyone serves me, he must follow me; and where I am, there shall my servant be also; if anyone serves me, the Father will honor him." (Jn. 12:23-26)

When Jesus says this, he has already brought the dead Lazarus from the grave. He stood at the open tomb of a man already far gone into death and corruption ("Lord, it stinks—he's been dead four days") and called the dead to life by his word: "Lazarus, come forth."

Jesus is preparing to go down into the grave himself. He is on his way to the cross.

The death and resurrection of Christ form God's greatest act of creation out of nothing. It is a work that seems absurd to "sensible" people who think that we can hope only to keep what we have, and so must cling to life and to our possessions:

And he began to teach them that the Son of man must suffer many things, and be rejected by the elders and the chief priests and the scribes, and be killed, and after three days rise again. And he said this plainly. And Peter took him, and began to rebuke him. But turning and seeing his disciples, he rebuked Peter, and said, "Get behind me, Satan! For you are not on the side of God, but of men." (Mk. 8:31-33)

The cross is the death of all sensible hope and the destruction of everything that humanity considers valuable. For the Romans who executed Jesus, crucifixion was a shameful death for slaves and rebels. It could not be inflicted upon Roman citizens. "Lay the cross on the slave" was the traditional way of sentencing. And for the Jews, death by crucifixion was considered especially unclean:

Christ redeemed us from the curse of the law, having become a curse for us—for it is written, "Cursed be every one who hangs on a tree." (Gal. 3:13)

As Christ hangs on the cross, it is as if the universe had returned to the darkness that was before creation:

> There was darkness over the whole land until the ninth hour,
> while the sun's light failed. (Lk. 23:44-45)

And on the Sabbath, the creator of the world rests in the darkness of the grave.

This is the heaviest condemnation of human sin and the clearest sign of the brokenness of creation. God made the world good, but the world has turned from God. As we will discuss in the next chapters, biological evolution is a theory which is strongly supported by scientific evidence. The idea of *progress*, however, is something else again. The notion that we are getting better and better on our own, or that we have outgrown the idea of obedience to the God who has created us, is sheer illusion. By condemning Jesus to death, the best that humanity can do by itself stands condemned. The fine religious piety of Jewish monotheism and the efficient political and legal system of Rome confront their creator—and kill him. The death of Jesus Christ destroys human pride. It brings to the sharpest focus the absurdity of believing that we are evolving automatically to higher and higher ethical states. And if we object that we have made a great deal of moral progress in the past two thousand years, Hiroshima and Auschwitz and Gulag, *apartheid* and abortion clinics and the missiles in our silos, will remind us how far we have progressed.

Wisdom which is merely human, worldly power structures and attempts to exploit the powers of nature, stand convicted by the cross of Christ:

> Yet among the mature we do impart wisdom, although it is not
> a wisdom of this age or of the rulers of this age, who are doomed
> to pass away. But we impart a secret and hidden wisdom of
> God, which God decreed before the ages for our glorification.
> None of the rulers of this age understood this; for if they had,
> they would not have crucified the Lord of glory. (1 Cor. 2:6-8)

In speaking of the "rulers," Paul has in mind demonic forces which we might consider mythological. But there is a truth which is deeper than the language which is used to express it. There *are* cosmic powers which enslave us—powers like nuclear energy or political and economic systems. These are not evil in themselves, but they are forces for evil in our lives because we allow them to be evil when we attempt to use them to accomplish our own self-serving goals.

All of that, all our dreams of exploiting and ruling the world and of using one another, are torn to shreds at Golgotha. There is nothing for us to boast about. All hope is gone, and our fear drives us to hide from the world.

> On the evening of that day, the first day of the week, the doors being shut where the disciples were, for fear of the Jews, Jesus came and stood among them and said to them, "Peace be with you." When he had said this, he showed them his hands and his side. Then the disciples were glad when they saw the Lord. (Jn. 20:19-20)

Jesus was dead, and it is impossible that the dead should rise. And Jesus is alive. Just as it is impossible that something should be made from nothing—and God created the universe out of nothing. The resurrection of the dead is creation out of nothing.

The risen Christ is the beginning of a new creation and the head of a new humanity. "Therefore," says St. Paul, "if anyone is in Christ, he is a new creation; the old has passed away, behold, the new has come" (2 Cor. 5:17). "For it is the God who said, 'Let light shine out of darkness,' who has shone in our hearts to give the light of the knowledge of the glory of God in the face of Christ" (2 Cor. 4:6).

The new life comes to us entirely through the grace of God. That was one of the great themes of Martin Luther—salvation is *by grace alone*. There is nothing in us that merits salvation. God did not decide to save us because he saw some tremendous potential for good within us. No, "While we were still weak, at the right time Christ died for the ungodly" (Rom. 5:6). We are declared righteous by the creative Word of God, though it seemed impossible that we should ever be righteous. "Justification by grace alone" is another way of saying "Creation out of nothing." The God who creates out of nothing is the God "who justifies the ungodly" (Rom. 4:5).

The grace of God is accepted by faith—the trust that God will do what seems impossible in human estimation. "By faith," the writer to the Hebrews says, "we understand that the world was created by the word of God, so that what is seen was made out of things which do not appear" (Heb. 11:3). And St. Paul speaks in a similar way of justification:

> That is why it depends on faith, in order that the promise may rest on grace and be guaranteed to all his descendants—not only to the adherents of the law but also to those who share the faith of Abraham, for he is the father of us all, as it is written, "I have made you the father of many nations"—in the presence of the God in whom he believed, who gives life to the dead and calls into existence the things that do not exist. In hope he believed against hope. . . . (Rom. 4:16-18)

We have talked in these last three chapters about the trademark of God, the thing that characterizes God's actions toward the world. God is the one who creates out of nothing. God is the one who raises the dead. God is the one who justifies the ungodly. *All of God's work is creation.* God's work is done in spite of obstacles, even though it seems impossible by human standards.

To say it in another way, God is the one who does surprising things, and who works in surprising ways. To give the child of promise to aged, barren Sarah, to make the shepherd boy David the King of Israel and ancestor of the Messiah—those are the kinds of things that God does. So the glory of God shines forth most brightly from the gallows, and pilgrims still go to the Church of the Resurrection in Jerusalem to revere a tomb where life arose.

That is the mark which God places upon Christians—upon the new humanity:

> But you are a chosen race, a royal priesthood, a holy nation, God's own people, that you may declare the wonderful deeds of him who called you out of darkness into his marvelous light. Once you were no people but now you are God's people; once you had not received mercy but now you have received mercy. (1 Pet. 2:9-10)

So Christians are able, like Abraham, to "hope against hope." They need not simply hope that God will put the pieces back together after something has gone wrong, but that God will do something new.

It is possible then to look forward in hope to the consummation of God's new creation, when death and destruction will be no more. So the seer of the Book of Revelation "saw a new heaven and a new earth; for the first heaven and the first earth had passed away, and the sea was no more. . . . And he who sat upon the throne said, 'Behold, I make all things new' " (Rev. 21:1, 5). The sea, the cosmic Deep that symbolizes chaos and death (as in Genesis 1:2) will finally be done away with.

That God is always at work, in love creating out of nothing, is the heart of the biblical doctrine of creation. And that is the *kind* of thing that we find in Darwin's evolutionary theory of natural selection and "survival of the fittest." Evolution, the development of life and finally the development of human beings who can bear the image of God, takes place through death and extinction. The very powers that seem most hostile to life are broken by God, who brings life out of them. This is an even more profound idea of creation out of nothing than the idea that there is simply nothing there, a vacuum, and that God makes something appear in that vacuum.

All that is not to say that we are to read the Bible as a textbook of biology to find out the details of evolution. And it is not to say that death and extinction are good, any more than the murder of Christ was good. God creates in spite of evil.

And it is remarkable that, in spite of the surprising and even shocking way that God works, creation is governed in accordance with the wisdom of God. And since God gives wisdom as his gift to humanity, it is possible for us to understand the world.

> For it is he who gave me unerring knowledge of what exists,
> to know the structure of the world and the activity of the
>   elements;
> the beginning and end and middle of times,

the alternations of the solstices and the changes of the seasons,
the cycles of the year and the constellations of the stars,
the natures of animals and the tempers of wild beasts,
the powers of spirits and the reasonings of men,
the varieties of plants and the virtues of roots;
I learned both what is secret and what is manifest,
for wisdom, the fashioner of all things, taught me.

(Wis. 7:17-22)

God has made us able to understand the Big Bang and the genetic code, and those are next on our agenda.

CHAPTER FIVE

"When the Morning Stars Sang Together"

FOR HALF A CENTURY we've known that we live in an expanding universe. It was in 1929 that the American astronomer Edwin Hubble announced his discovery of this expansion. Since then, the evidence that the entire universe is changing and evolving has continued to accumulate. The universe is changing from one kind of state to another. Scientists can thus speak about the beginning of the universe, and try to predict how it will end. Theologians and scientists can't help meeting one another in their explorations of the beginning and the end, and the only question is whether they will meet as enemies or as partners in exploration.

Attempts to understand the structure of the universe did not, of course, begin in this century. People had always noticed, together with the individual stars of night, the Milky Way, a broad, hazy band through the constellations which is most prominent in the summer sky. When Galileo turned his first crude telescopes on the Milky Way in the seventeenth century, he found it to consist of a vast number of stars, too distant and faint to be seen individually with the naked eye. The shape of this broad band of stars suggests that we are within a large, disc-shaped distribution of matter. It wasn't until the early part of this century that the full extent of our galaxy became known. It turns out that the galactic

33

disc is about a hundred thousand light-years across and about a tenth that thick.

(A *light-year* is the distance that light travels in a year, about 6,000,000,000,000 [six trillion] miles. Just the need to use a unit of this size points up the immensity of the universe.)

But is the Milky Way the whole universe? Some astronomers thought so, but others argued that some of the "clouds" of stars which had been found in space were not within the Milky Way at all, but were separate galaxies in their own right. In order to resolve this dispute, it was necessary to find a way to measure the distances to these star clouds. This was made possible by Henrietta Leavitt's discovery of a way in which certain very bright stars could be used as distance indicators. When this method was used, the star clouds in question turned out to be far outside the Milky Way. The great galaxy in Andromeda, for example, is over two million light-years away. It became clear that our Milky Way is only one among a large number of galaxies which are spread throughout the universe.

(We should note, too, that when we look out to such great distances, we are also looking back in time. The light which will strike your eye if you go out and look at the Andromeda galaxy tonight began its journey over two million years ago. The vast *size* of the universe which we've discovered carries with it an indication of the universe's tremendous age.)

The next discovery was even more revolutionary. Hubble found that the light from distant galaxies was changed in a definite way, so that the farther away a galaxy was, the redder its light appeared in photographs. The most natural explanation of this was the Doppler effect, a change in the length of waves when their source is in motion with respect to an observer. If the source is moving toward the observer, the waves will be "squeezed together" and shortened, while recession of the source will produce longer waves. This shift in wavelength, and thus pitch, can be detected with sound waves—stand beside the highway and listen to the change in pitch of a car's horn as it passes. When we are concerned with light waves, the effect shows itself in a change of color, and this is what Hubble had found in the light waves from distant galaxies.

This "redshift" of light from the galaxies thus indicates an overall expansion of the universe. Every galaxy is moving away from every other one, and the most distant ones are moving the fastest. We may imagine that all the galaxies were confined to a small region of space at some time in the distant past and then exploded outward. The galaxies which were moving fastest in the beginning would naturally have gotten the farthest. By measuring the distances to the galaxies and their speeds, it is possible for us to work backwards and get an estimate of the time which has elapsed since the initial explosion, or Big Bang. This number is still uncertain, largely because of the difficulty in measuring such distances, but the time since the beginning of the universal expansion seems to have been between ten and twenty billion years. These figures give us at least a rough idea of what is sometimes referred to as "the age of the universe."

Yet we should remember that we have been talking in the last paragraph about a *model* of the universe. Models are extremely valuable in helping us to understand complicated systems, but they *are* models, and are not to be taken literally. If we didn't observe this caution with the "explosion model" which we've just described, we might become unduly concerned about what is at the "center of the universe," or about the fact that some observer could be in space completely "outside the universe." More sophisticated models of the universe, involving such notions as curved space, make clear that it has no "center" or "outside."

But is this extrapolation back to some tremendous explosion involving the entire universe really legitimate? After all, our observations cover only a tiny fraction of the history of the universe. Fortunately, we now have more direct evidence that the Big Bang actually took place. When the matter which makes up the universe was much more tightly squeezed together than it is today, the temperature would have been very high and there would have been a great deal of radiation present. The universe cooled down as it expanded from this "fireball" condition, but calculations indicate that the radiation which was present then should still pervade the universe, though now greatly weakened. In 1965, scientists working on radio equipment developed to communicate with earth satellites confirmed this prediction. The detection of this faint radio "noise" provides strong evidence that the universe was once at a state of very high temperature, with its matter densely packed together.

It was, we think, in the very early stages of this fireball, when the universe was only minutes old, that a critical "cooking" of the chemical elements took place. Temperatures were so high then that new atoms could be formed in the collisions between particles. In fact, many of the features of the present universe seem to have been determined when it was quite young. Georges Lemaître, the Belgian priest who did some of the most important pioneering work in this study of the evolution of the universe, expressed it in this way:

> The evolution of the world can be compared to a display of fireworks that has just ended: some few red wisps, ashes, and smoke. Standing on a cooled cinder, we see the slow fading of the suns, and we try to recall the vanished brilliance of the origin of the worlds.

Some of the atoms which exist in the universe today, atoms which were built in these first minutes, give us direct evidence about what went on in that period. But human imagination is not content to stop short of the beginning. Scientists have tried to use the scientific laws and equations which they have discovered to push back as close as possible to the very start of the cosmic expansion, "the beginning of time." We can go back in imagination to a fantastic epoch, when the universe was only a minute fraction of a second old, and when all the stars and galaxies within range of our present telescopes were squeezed into a space smaller than a present-day atom.

And if we attempt to push back beyond that time, the mathematical equations which are used to describe the universe break down and give nonsense. The laws of nature themselves seem to fail when we approach the beginning.

It may be, of course, that we simply don't understand the laws of nature well enough, and that only our naive models fail under these extreme conditions. Or it may be that the laws of nature are (if we may put it this way) less "ambitious" than we think. Perhaps they don't describe all phenomena completely, and the fact that they don't work at the beginning is an illustration of this.

Or it may be that the laws of nature themselves should be thought of as coming into being at the beginning of the universe. The Bible speaks of creation taking place through Christ, the "Word" or "Reason" of God (Jn. 1:1-5), and says that in Christ "all things hold together" (Col. 1:17). The creative Word of God is the source of the pattern which we call the laws of nature, whether we want to think of those laws as "beginning" at some time in the past or not. In any case, considerations about what happened in the first instant of creation, let alone before, will always be somewhat speculative.

"Where were you when I laid the f   n of the earth?" God demanded of Job,

> Tell me, if you have unde
> Who determined its me   surely you know!
> Or who stretched   upon it?
> On what were its bases sunk,
> or who laid its cornerstone,
> when the morning stars sang together,
> and all the sons of God shouted for joy? (Job 38:4-7)

In spite of all the knowledge we've gained, we can still try to exercise some humility.

Now we turn from our flight backward in time and come toward the present. The formation of our earth, and the development of life upon it, lie many years down the road from the fireball. As we come closer to the present, the course of events becomes clearer, though considerable uncertainty remains about some of the things we shall discuss.

If we could watch a speeded-up film of the universe from its beginning, a rather dull, dark period would elapse after the fireball. The hydrogen and helium gas simply thins out and cools down. But gravitational forces in this gas cause it to break up and condense into gigantic clumps—how, we're not exactly sure. These galaxy-sized clumps of gas themselves break up into smaller clumps, which will condense into stars. Our dark movie screen comes to life as these young stars contract, heat up and begin to emit radiation. Soon their interiors reach temperatures of tens of millions of degrees, hot enough to ignite the fusion reactions which power our sun. In these reactions, heavier atoms are built up—atoms of elements like carbon and oxygen and phosphorus, the things which are essential for life. The material of our bodies was formed in the stars.

But it is not only stars which form from the giant clouds of gas and dust. We may picture such a cloud with a newly formed star blazing at its center, surrounded by the debris of its birth. In some cases, this debris may be blown away into space by the force of the star's radiation, and in others it may be taken up to form a companion star. But sometimes this remaining material, circling around a young star, will condense into a system of planets like our solar system. And some of those planets may resemble our earth.

How common an occurrence is that? We simply don't know. Our own planetary system is the only one in the universe that we know of for sure. There is some evidence for other planetary systems, and some astronomers believe that there is a large number of such systems in our galaxy. At present, however, we simply don't know enough to be able to answer the question with any certainty.

In our own solar system, we know of course that at least one planet has conditions suitable for life. The earth formed with the right materials, and at the right distance from the sun, to serve as a home for the kind of life that we know of. The evolution of life on earth will be the subject of the next chapter.

When did the earth form? We have seen that current estimates of the age of the universe are between ten and twenty billion years. The solar system will naturally be younger. We can get a more precise estimate by examining the proportions of various radio-active elements in the earth's crust and on other bodies which we can probe in the solar system. Each radioactive element has a characteristic rate at which it decays, and the ones which decay fastest will tend to be less abundant because they die off more quickly. For example, the type of uranium which can be used to make atomic bombs decays more quickly than the kind that can't, and so is (fortunately) less abundant. Knowing the decay rates and the proportions of elements which are present today, we can estimate the time that has passed since these atoms were formed. It appears from such calculations that the earth is about four and a half billion years old.

(As with any scientific calculation, certain assumptions have to be made. Here we have to know the rates at which radioactive decay took place in the *past*, and we have to make reasonable assumptions about the amounts of various kinds of atoms which were present to begin with. The general consistency of many experiments and observations on this subject suggests that our assumptions are not too far wrong.)

When the earth had formed, gases squeezed out of it went to form an atmosphere for the planet. (This was rather different from our present atmosphere, since there were not yet any green plants to provide oxygen.) The water on the earth's surface probably also came from within the planet. Continents and seas formed, though they were continents and seas with positions and shapes quite different from those of the present.

The major revolution still to come on earth, however, was not the movement of the continents but the development of life. No traces remain of the first living organisms, and we are still far from understanding exactly how they originated. But scientists have carried out experiments in which they attempt to duplicate the physical and chemical conditions of the primitive earth. In these experiments, simple chemicals like water, hydrogen, methane and ammonia are combined. From them it is possible to form amino acids, the basic molecular building blocks for life, as well as other molecules which are important in biological processes. These chemicals might have formed a thin "soup" in pools on the surface of the earth. Over millions of years, the chemical combinations needed to give rise to self-reproducing molecules could have taken place. Life arose.

All that we have described so far was done without any thought at all on the part of the universe itself. That was to change, however. The universe was about to become conscious of itself.

CHAPTER SIX

Dust That Dreams

It was hard for people to believe that species could die—but that's what the fossils said. Fossils had been known for a long time—remains of plants and animals embedded in the rocks. Some looked like plants and animals alive today, but many were of quite different kinds—no human being has ever seen a living dinosaur. What were people to make of these extinct species?

For a long time it was hard to believe that they *were* extinct. During the seventeenth and eighteenth centuries, people seem to have forgotten the biblical emphasis on God's creation in spite of death and destruction—creation out of nothing. Instead, they emphasized God's maintenance of the *status quo,* so that it was very hard to believe that species could have vanished. But exploration of the earth showed that those missing creatures weren't hiding anywhere. The death of species was a fact.

More than that—new species had appeared. When geologists began to explore the earth's crust systematically, they found much of it to be in layers. Material had been slowly deposited over the ages and compressed into rock, perhaps on the floors of ancient seas. These layers of rock contain shells and skeletons of ancient creatures, as well as other evidence from the past. Roughly speaking, the lower layers contain the older fossils. The very oldest rocks contain no fossils at all. Those around three billion years old may have the remains of one-celled organisms. As we move toward the present, we find more complex creatures.

Fossils of one type may appear at some point in this geological record, last for some time, and then not be found above a certain layer. Species are "born" and species "die"—that much is certain.

But we can also tell that different species aren't isolated from one another. There are changes in fossils from one layer to another which suggest transformations from one type to another. The evidence isn't as clear as we'd like. It's important to realize that only a minute fraction of creatures have died under conditions which allow their remains to be fossilized. Of those, the fossils may have been destroyed during the millions of years which have passed, or we may simply never find them. The fossil record is incomplete, like a few pages torn at random from the pages of a history book.

So we often don't find the connections which should exist between species. People speak of "missing links," and many *are* missing. But we can read the general pattern of the history of life, and it is a history of transformation from one species to another. *Evolution* has taken place.

By the mid-1800s there had been a good deal of discussion of the idea of evolution. People had been pretty well convinced by the geological evidence that the earth was very old, and that some plant and animal species had disappeared while others had arisen. But there was no clear idea of *how* evolution could have happened. What makes evolution work?

Most of us would probably like to think that we've evolved to such an advanced state because our ancestors *tried* very hard. We want hard work to be rewarded, and it's natural for us to think that evolution should operate in that way. According to this idea, the characteristics acquired by a plant or animal during its life can be passed on to its descendants. An animal that stretches its neck to eat leaves at the tops of trees would pass on a slightly lengthened neck to its children. If that took place generation after generation, the giraffe's neck could be the result.

It's a simple idea, and one which has sometimes been quite

popular—but it doesn't seem to work that way. Careful experiments and observations of plant and animal breeding have not shown evidence of such transmission of acquired characteristics. Successive generations of blacksmiths are not endowed with more and more powerful arms at birth.

Then what is the answer? The fundamental insight into the mechanism of evolution was achieved in the mid-nineteenth century by Charles Darwin. The title of his famous book of 1859 expresses the basic idea: *On the Origin of Species by Means of Natural Selection; or, the Preservation of Favored Races in the Struggle for Life.*

Darwin had been the naturalist on the world-circling, five-year voyage of H.M.S. *Beagle.* He had been able to observe the fossils and the distribution of plants and animals in many environments, and returned convinced that evolution had taken place. The "how" question still remained. Then Darwin's reading suggested to him that the pressure of excess population could play a role. If there is a greater population of animals than can be supported in a given environment, some will not survive. On the average, those best fitted for survival *will* survive, and will be able to produce offspring.

Now there are always variations among members of a species. Some will have longer necks than others, some will be quicker and some smarter. Those creatures having variations which favor their survival will pass them on to their offspring. In times of low rainfall, when foliage was scarce, animals with slightly longer necks would have been able to reach the higher leaves on trees. They would, on the average, leave more descendants—descendants with necks slightly longer than average. This continued selection process, generation after generation, could have produced the giraffe.

This mechanism of evolution is sometimes described as "survival of the fittest." That phrase should be used with some care. What constitutes "fitness" depends on the environment in which the organism finds itself. There is nothing absolutely good about having a long neck. The neck of the giraffe evolved in that way because it gave certain advantages in a particular environment. An environmental change hazardous to long necks could wipe out the giraffe.

An example of this principle is seen among humans. There is a modification of the red blood cells which leads to a disease called sickle-cell anemia. This hereditary trait is carried by some black people in the United States. Here it is a variation which makes life more difficult, and we may wonder why it has survived for many generations. It turns out that a form of this trait gives increased resistance to malaria, a disease which is a serious problem in Africa. While the sickle-cell trait has disadvantages, its "incomplete" form has a net survival value in Africa, and thus contributes to "fitness."

Thus adaptation to the particular environment defines fitness for a given population. When the environment changes, so do the requirements for fitness.

The destruction of species and the appearance of new ones may involve simply a slow fading out of the old through lowered reproduction rates or failure in competition for food. There does not have to be much outright violence. But evolutionary change does take place through death and extinction. Even without physical suffering—and there has been plenty of that—there is a sadness about the departure of these distant relatives of ours. Even though we wouldn't want to meet a saber-toothed tiger or *Tyrannosaurus rex* in a dark alley, we can regret their passing.

The appearance and disappearance of species in the fossil record is the basic evidence for biological evolution. But there are many other things which argue for the theory. Darwin pointed out that the selective breeding of plants and animals carried out for several thousand years by humans shows that the character of organisms can be changed. (Several pages of his book are devoted to pigeon breeding.) The corn hybrids which are so important today are a tiny piece of evidence for evolution.

But can new *types* of organisms, new species, be produced by selective breeding? Of course we can't turn mice into monkeys. If nothing else, there isn't enough time. Over three billion years elapsed between the origin of life and the appearance of human beings on earth. But, in a modest way, new species have been developed. A species is defined as a group of organisms which can interbreed to produce viable and fertile offspring, but which is not able so to interbreed with organisms outside this group. If we use this criterion, botanists have been able to develop several new species of plants. The plants have been so changed by selective breeding that they are infertile with the original parent stock.

If all life on earth has evolved from a single source, we would expect there to be close relationships between different species, living and extinct. This is indeed the case. These relationships appear in our large-scale anatomy and in the molecular makeup of our cells. The human arm, the flipper of the whale, and the wing of a bird all show the same basic bone structure, developed for different tasks in different animals. And the hemoglobin in our blood shows a 99 percent similarity in chemical composition to that of our nearest relatives among the apes.

Other relationships are seen when we examine the growth of animals in the womb. At a sufficiently early stage of development, it is almost impossible to tell the difference between a human embryo and that of another mammal. In our development from a fertilized egg we reveal our kinship with our remote ancestors, going through the same kind of embryological development that they did.

We're especially interested, of course, in what this all has to do with the human race. Darwin's theory of evolution would not have caused nearly the stir that it did if it had exempted the human race. It's the idea that *we*, the image of God, are the descendants of worms and the "cousins" of apes, that seems so offensive. Some of the theological problems with evolution will be discussed in later chapters. For now, we want to concentrate on what evolutionary theory really says about us.

We did not descend from apes. Present-day chimpanzees and gorillas are the product of evolution, just as we are. The evidence which we have today suggests that apes and humans have descended from a common ancestor. The evolutionary lines which would lead to human beings and to present-day apes branched off from one another sometime between ten and twenty-five million years ago. (There is some uncertainty because dating by fossils gives results different from those obtained by studying the chemical differences of ape and human blood. This is just one of many indications that there are still large gaps in our understanding of human origins.)

Modern humanity, *Homo sapiens* ("wise human"), didn't appear as soon as this branching took place. Fossils discovered especially in Africa show a gradual change from apelike creatures (called *Ramapithecus*) to those of around a hundred thousand years ago which differ very little from modern humans. By this time, *Homo sapiens* had spread over much of the earth.

There was not, however, unerring progress toward modern humanity. Other evolutionary branches divided off after the split from the line leading to the apes. None of these nearer cousins of ours has survived to the present. One of the most recent branches, a subspecies of *Homo sapiens*, was the famous Neanderthal man. (They were not nearly as brutish in appearance as many pictures suggest.) Extinction has taken place within the human species itself—the Neanderthals died out about thirty thousand years ago.

While we can learn a lot from ancient bones and stone tools, there are many things about our ancestors which aren't preserved. We don't know, for example, when spoken language, one of the chief things distinguishing us from other animals, developed. We don't know when our ancestors first became conscious of *themselves*—when they realized that they were thinking. We do know that by fifty thousand years ago, the cave-dwellers had some sense of ideas that we think of as religious. Objects that they buried with their dead suggest some idea of survival after death. Then, within a period of time which is tiny in comparison with the age of the earth, came an extremely rapid development: cave paintings, agriculture, building, law, and science. Cultural as well as purely biological evolution has become important. And within the past few centuries, humanity has become able to understand its evolution, and even to exert some control over it.

For at about the same time that Darwin was publishing his theory, the Moravian monk Gregor Mendel was carrying out experiments on plant breeding which established the basis of the modern science of genetics. During the century since his work, scientists have discovered a great deal about the molecular mechanisms by which hereditary information is encoded within each cell of a living organism. The pattern of basic building blocks which form long molecular strands within the cell can be regarded as a language—the "genetic code." This allows the cell's molecular mechanism to carry the information necessary for the synthesis of the chemicals which the cells require. In particular, the information which enables the cell to replicate itself is encoded in the molecular structure of the cell. This genetic information from father and mother is shared in the offspring, so that the species is continued.

For various reasons, however, there can be changes—*mutations* —in the genetic messages, and thus there will be slightly new characteristics introduced in the offspring. Natural selection by the environment is able to work on such variations, reinforcing some generation after generation and suppressing others in accord with the demands of the environment. Thus variations among genetic messages make possible an immense variety of organisms, and natural selection by the environment from among this variety has produced the astonishing range of organisms which have inhabited the earth until today.

At the same time, these genetic messages show the underlying unity of life on earth. It seems that the same genetic code is used by almost all organisms on earth—we all "speak the same language." This supports the idea that all terrestrial life has originated from one source.

The basic atoms of the earth's crust and seas have come together to form men and women who can contemplate their own past and dream of their own future. We are made of the dust of the earth, as Genesis says. The theory of evolution speaks in a similar way. But biology alone does not speak of the fact that we are made to hear the Word of God, and to be in a loving relationship with the creator of the universe.

We are dust that dreams—and sometimes we have nightmares.

Something has happened to God's good creation, and the fact that we don't understand our origins, that our understanding of the evolution of the world and our faith in God as the creator sometimes seem in conflict, is a symbol of this. But the remedy is here, founded in the unity of life. For into this race which has wandered from the way, a race descended from ancient sea creatures and apelike ancestors, is to be born the very creator of the world. Like our ancestors who huddled in the caves against the winters of the Ice Age, Jesus lies in Bethlehem's cave:

> Heaven cannot hold him,
> Nor earth sustain;
> Heaven and earth shall flee away
> When he comes to reign;
> In the bleak midwinter
> A stable place sufficed
> The Lord God Almighty,
> Jesus Christ.

Christina Georgina Rossetti

CHAPTER SEVEN

The Battle of the Century

THE RUNNING BATTLE over the teaching of evolution and creation in public schools has been one of the biggest religious news items of recent years. In fact, probably the only time a lot of Americans ever hear about the Bible is when accounts of this dispute over education are in the newspapers or on television. And this has been going on for a long time. The Scopes "monkey trial" in Tennessee, involving a challenge to a state law which prohibited the teaching of evolution in public schools, took place in 1925. The intensity of these controversies has varied over the years, but the conflict shows no sign of disappearing.

Public education has certainly not been the only area of our lives in which the creation-evolution issue has surfaced. Clarence Darrow, the pro-evolution lawyer in the Scopes trial, had been the defense attorney in the celebrated Leopold-Loeb murder case the previous year. He argued there that his clients' behavior was determined by inheritance and environment, and was able to save them from hanging. Such arguments that our behavior is determined by our make-up can easily be connected with evolutionary theory. "If we are descended from lower animals," a person may argue, "it's hardly surprising if we act like them some of the time. And how can we be blamed for that?"

Evolution has also been either called upon, or blamed for,

things much greater than the crimes of individuals. The idea of "survival of the fittest" has been used to justify "Social Darwinism," the idea that weak and powerless members of society should simply be allowed to suffer and die because they are clearly not fit to survive. In fact, the argument may continue, we have a duty to let this happen, so that these "inferior" people will not weaken the race. (If this sounds a bit like Nazi thinking, that is no coincidence!) The evolution of humanity has also been an important part of Marxist ideology, and today helps to supply the official antireligious teaching in the Soviet Union with ammunition.

"Evolution versus creation"—what really are the basic reasons for so much disagreement and unpleasantness? Have the issues been understood clearly?

First we have to make sure that the language we're using is clear. Often the issue is stated as I just presented it—"evolution versus creation." Either you think that life has evolved or you believe that God created the world. But a person just doesn't have to make that choice. There are millions of Christians who confess God as "maker of all that is," *and* who accept the evolutionary account of the way that life developed on earth. We have seen that some of the early teachers of the church interpreted Genesis in ways that left room for evolution. Furthermore, the evolutionary development of life through competition and death bears the divine "creation out of nothing" trademark which the Bible reveals. So strictly speaking, "evolution versus creation" is not the issue.

But for many people, "creation" does not mean only the doctrine that God created the universe out of nothing and still sustains it, but also a specific interpretation of how creation took place. This is based on a rather literal reading of Genesis. According to this line of thought, God created all the biological "types" immediately, perhaps in six literal days. From this point on I will refer to that sort of position, which *is* opposed to evolution, as "creationism." Creationism is one way of trying to express the Christian doctrine of creation, but it is not the only way. Nor do I think it is the best way.

But now let's focus on some specific problems, and try to

see what is at stake with them. Many Christians, and not only "creationists," have trouble with some aspects of evolution, and there are also people who have problems with the Christian doctrine of creation. Some of these difficulties will be mentioned, together with some comments on them.

A very basic argument is the need to take seriously what the Bible tells us. If Scripture says that the world was created in six days, that ought to settle it for Christians.

It is true that the Bible needs to be taken with complete seriousness. This means that we have to be willing to hear what it says, not just what we've always thought it said, or what we'd like it to say. When studying the early chapters of Genesis, we need to ask if they are intended to be read as literal history, like a history of the United States since the Civil War. In chapter 3 we saw that this doesn't seem to be the case. The fact that there are *two* creation accounts in Genesis, describing the origins of things in quite different ways, suggests that we have to deal there with a symbolic use of language. (This is a far different thing from saying that these accounts are "wrong.") As we have seen before, the language which is used there does not at all conflict with evolution—"Let the waters bring forth swarms of living creatures" and God creating humanity "of dust from the ground." Accepting the biblical witness doesn't mean that a person must reject evolution, though she or he may choose to do so.

Another question that is raised by evolution has to do with the dignity and moral responsibility of human beings. What can be expected of men and women if they are regarded as only thinly disguised apes?

The fact that evolution happens gradually doesn't mean that there have been no dramatic changes. (In fact, some evolutionary scientists are now arguing that most evolutionary change occurs in relatively short bursts.) The development of the reflective consciousness of human beings was probably the most dramatic development since the beginning of life itself. We are not only conscious, but we are aware of, and reflect upon, our consciousness. Other animals know—we know that we know. (There may be

relatives of ours, dolphins or chimpanzees, which have some degree
of reflective consciousness, but at this point that is still rather
speculative.) Our ability to think in this way makes us qualitatively
different from our ancestors, who couldn't. Because of this ability,
it is possible for us to speak of morals and ethics for human beings
in ways that would not make sense for cows or chipmunks.

Evolution need not mean that there are no important differences between human beings and other animals. But we also want
to remember that, in the Christian view, dignity and responsibility
come first and foremost from God, and from the fact that God's
word has been directed to us: "Let us make humanity in our image,
after our likeness, and let them have dominion. . . ." Our worth
is due to the fact that God assigns us worth, and we have moral
responsibilities because God gives them to us. If we are not in
the right relationship with God, we are no more than the dust
from which we were made: "Man that is in honour, and under-
standeth not, is like the beasts that perish" (Ps. 49:20, KJV).

There is another dimension to this that we dare not forget.
It's expressed nicely in the following poem by that well-known
author Anonymous, entitled "Darwin's Mistake":

> Three monkeys sat in a coconut tree,
> Discussing things as they're said to be.
> Said one to the others, "Now listen, you two,
> There's a certain rumor that can't be true,
> That man descended from our noble race.
> The very idea is a disgrace.
>
> No monkey ever deserted his wife,
> Starved her babies or ruined her life.
> And another thing you will never see
> A monkey build a fence around a coconut tree
> And let the coconuts go to waste,
> Forbidding all other monkeys to taste.
>
> If I put a fence around this tree,
> Starvation would force you to steal from me.
> Here's another thing a monkey won't do,

Go out at night and get on a stew,
And use a gun or a club or knife
To take some other monkey's life.
Yes, man descended, the ornery cuss—
But, brother, he didn't descend from us."

There is a sense in which we are *worse* than other animals. This can never be an excuse to avoid responsibility for our actions, but it does show that we shouldn't speak *too* easily of our superiority to the "lower animals."

Another challenge which some people have felt from Darwinian evolution involves the question of whether or not there is any purpose to life, or to the whole universe. This is a challenge felt by many people besides Christians, for almost everyone is repelled by the idea that existence is fundamentally pointless. But that idea still has to be faced honestly.

We discussed in the previous chapter Darwin's theory that the transformation of species takes place because small random variations make some members of a species better suited for survival in the environment in which they find themselves than are other members. The basic task is survival in one's environment. The blind fish which have "degenerated" to suit the environment of Mammoth Cave or the tapeworm which lives as an intestinal parasite in human beings are just as "fit," and in this sense just as advanced, as are human beings.

But if this is the case, it seems as if we can't talk about human beings as the most advanced product of evolution—or about evolutionary progress at all. Where is evolution heading, then? Is there any goal, any purpose to all this business of big bangs and radiation, genes and evolution, or do life and the universe just wander along aimlessly until everything spreads out, cools down, and dies?

If we restrict ourselves purely to the standpoint of evolutionary biology, the only purpose or goal of life and evolution is survival. But we need not restrict ourselves to such a standpoint. There are real senses in which human beings are superior to other animals, but that is a value judgment made from outside the sphere of pure biology. Human beings are rational and possess reflective consciousness. These are important aspects of the "image of God" in humanity, for it is through them that humanity is able to "have dominion." Those qualities make us superior to other animals that we know of. However, we cannot say, as a purely biological statement, that evolution has taken place in order to produce our rationality or reflective consciousness—whatever may be God's purpose. The only way in which we can look at things from God's point of view, and discern God's purpose, is to study the revelation in Scripture which is centered in Jesus Christ.

Perhaps, when all this is said, we still have an uneasy feeling about evolution. It doesn't seem appropriate for God's creation to come through competition and extinction, and it doesn't seem right for the creatures who bear the image of God to be descended from the beasts. But that is a difficulty we have not just with evolution but with all of God's creative work. We have seen that the characteristic mark of this work is to bring something new out of what seems like a completely unlikely and unpromising situation. And in chapter 10 we will talk about the climax of this work—what St. Paul calls the "folly" of the cross (1 Cor. 1:18).

So far we have talked about some of the problems which people have with evolution. There are also difficulties which people have with the Christian teaching concerning creation, or with ways in which that treatment has been presented to them. Many people who are familiar with scientific developments are put off by "creationist" claims that a person has to reject evolution and accept a creationist interpretation of Genesis. Besides representing an inadequate picture of what Christian teaching is, the creationist view presents an unnecessary obstacle which can keep non-Christians from really hearing the gospel. If people in today's world are to take the gospel seriously, the church must develop its theology in a way which takes proper account of our scientific understanding of the universe and of its history.

It has also been argued that the problems which our society has with our destruction of the environment and ecological imbalance can be traced to the biblical idea that humanity is to "fill the earth and subdue it" (Gen. 1:28). We have to admit that there is some substance to this charge, for Christians often have assumed that humanity's dominion over the earth was simply a privilege, without any corresponding responsibility, and that we could do whatever we wished with the earth or with other living creatures. This is certainly not the biblical picture, for our "dominion" is to be exercised as God's representative—as God's image. Our attitude toward the creation is to be modeled on God's, an attitude of self-giving love. Our dominion is to be exercised in care and willingness to serve. Here an evolutionary understanding can help us in our responsibility. An awareness of our interconnection with the rest of creation can strengthen our desire to help in caring for the world.

There is another sort of criticism, however, with which we cannot agree, and that is the argument that the doctrine of creation is to be rejected because it allows humanity to be enslaved by God. (This was, for example, the complaint of Marx.) We may agree that the "slave" image is not a good one to represent humanity's relationship to God. But to revolt against being creatures, and to put ourselves or other creatures in place of the creator, is the fundamental sin. It is a violation of the First Commandment that "you shall have no other gods before Me." According to St. Paul, the sins which plague human beings have come "because they exchanged the truth about God for a lie and worshiped and served the creature rather than the Creator, who is blessed forever" (Rom. 1:25). If evolution is presented as something which frees us from being creatures of God, then it is being misunderstood and misused. And such misunderstanding is caused in part by Christians who insist that a person must choose *either* creation *or* evolution.

There will always remain tensions and controversies when we deal with the interaction of science and theology. We can try to reduce these tensions by approaching issues in an informed and honest way. But the work of restoration of the world, and of the healing of the brokenness which leads to misunderstanding, is the work of Christ. We will turn to Bethlehem and Calvary to see where God's activity in our world is most clear. But in order to appreciate the significance of that work, we must first look more closely at the brokenness of the world. Why is there evil in the universe? The next chapter will focus on this "mystery of iniquity."

CHAPTER EIGHT

A Chapter about Nothing

WE CAN'T UNDERSTAND EVIL, and are always disturbed when we have to try to make some kind of sense of its presence in our world. The question of Hell, of the final state of the wicked, is sure to provoke disagreement in many discussion groups in the church. And the problem of the *origin* of evil is even more obscure to us. If God is good, and if the universe which God created was good (as Genesis says), then why is the world full of sin and death?

One thing that we can't do is ignore the problem, for the presence of evil in the world is unmistakable. Even if the Bible taught nothing about it, Hitler and Stalin, slavery and racism in America and Hiroshima, would force us to admit that evil must be confronted. But still, why? Where did it come from?

A traditional answer to these questions, based on Genesis 3 and Romans 5, is the doctrine of the fall of humanity. According to this, the first man and woman, created in a perfect relationship with God, disobeyed his commandment. All their descendants were then tainted with this sin from birth. "In Adam's fall, sinned we all," the schoolbooks of an earlier generation would say. The spoiling of nature and the rule of death are to be traced to this first sin.

Sin came into the world through one person and death

through sin, and so death spread to all people because all people sinned. (Rom. 5:12)

And it's death that makes the problem unavoidable. People may try to convince themselves that they've outgrown the idea of sin, but they can't ignore death. No matter how "natural" we may tell ourselves that dying is, there will come the death of a son or wife or leader with tremendous gifts which will force us to say, "It isn't fair."

The theory of evolution made Christians face this question of the origin of evil anew, and to realize that the traditional answers weren't completely satisfactory. It wasn't just that the literal Garden of Eden was challenged, for one could always suppose that there had been, in the evolutionary development, some first couple that could be called human. But it was clear that death had been a reality in the world long before there were any human beings to fall into sin. In fact, death was the very thing that made evolution work—indeed, the thing that seemed to make life possible. What sort of theological understanding of the relationship between sin and death was possible in an evolutionary universe?

That is still a question which we must wrestle with. And evil will remain a mystery. You shouldn't expect from this chapter a single neat solution which will put the whole problem of evil in order. But there will be some ideas which may be helpful, and some possibilities for further thought.

What do we mean by sin? The word calls up to us adultery, murder, theft and so on, and those *are* sins. But they don't define for us what sin is. We might say that those things are "sins" with a small *s*—but what is Sin? One of the clearest answers to that is given by St. Paul in the first chapter of Romans:

Ever since the creation of the world his [God's] invisible nature, namely, his eternal power and deity, has been clearly perceived in the things that have been made. So they are without excuse; for although they knew God they did not honor him as God or give thanks to him, but they became futile in their thinking and their senseless minds were darkened. Claiming to be wise, they became fools, and exchanged the glory of the immortal God for images resembling mortal man or birds or animals or reptiles.

Therefore God gave them up in the lusts of their hearts to impurity, to the dishonoring of their bodies among themselves, because they exchanged the truth about God for a lie and worshiped and served the creature rather than the Creator, who is blessed forever! Amen. (Rom. 1:20-25)

The basic Sin is against the First Commandment—"You shall have no other gods before me." All other sins are a consequence of idolatry, of turning away from the creator to created things—and this includes turning inward toward ourselves.

God created everything, men and women and the whole universe, out of nothing, and keeps it in existence. Turning away from God, then, means turning toward nothing. And that is what evil is finally—nothing! That's why evil is so hard to understand and to deal with—there's nothing there! This doesn't at all make sin and evil trivial or to be taken lightly. When we consider evil, we can get the sickening feeling of vertigo that comes when we stare down into the blackness of the infinite depths of an abyss. Scripture speaks of the "Deep" and "The Outer Darkness" when it tells of the consequences of sin. Evil always turns out in the end to be just an attractive lie. But why do we continue to fall for this lie?

And the woman said to the serpent, "We may eat of the fruit of the trees of the garden; but God said, 'You shall not eat of the fruit of the tree which is in the midst of the garden, neither shall you touch it, lest you die.' " But the serpent said to the woman, "You will not die. For God knows that when you eat of it your eyes will be opened, and you will be like God, knowing good and evil." (Gen. 3:2-5)

And she ate, and the man ate—and we know how the story goes from there. It's a true story which describes how our alienation from one another and our death follow from our revolt against God. It is, in short, our story.

There is another version of the story of the Fall, less familiar than that of Genesis, in the Book of Ezekiel. Ezekiel 26-28 contains four blazing oracles against Tyre, the great and proud merchant city of the Mediterranean coast. In Ezekiel 28:11-19, a story of the creation and fall of the first human being, made perfect to live "on the holy mountain of God," is used to describe the fate of the Prince of Tyre, who has claimed divinity:

> Your heart was proud because of your beauty;
> you corrupted your wisdom for the sake of your splendor.
>
> . . . .
>
> so I brought forth fire from the midst of you;
> it consumed you, and I turned you to ashes upon the earth
> in the sight of all who saw you.
> All who know you among the peoples are appalled at you;
> you have come to a dreadful end and shall be no more forever.
>
> (Ez. 28:17-19)

Humanity in love with itself, turned in on itself, is cut off from God and from life. The pride and the fall are in each of us—"And you shall be no more forever."

But can we imagine this as history?

The evolutionary picture of human beings tells us that humanity had a very long prehistory. The human race emerged only after the transformation of many other species, from one-celled animals, fishes, and the common ancestor of apes and humans, to us. The first creatures we would want to label "human" would have been, mentally and spiritually, at a very immature level. But at some point there were creatures, men and women, who were at least dimly conscious that they were conscious. They were able to *reflect*—to be human. And it is certainly possible that it is at this point that they became aware of God, and able to "hear" the Word of God addressed to them: "Have dominion."

We can only guess about that. There can be no scientific *proof* that things happened in that way. We can find the bones and flint tools of early humans, but their poetry or their prayers are not preserved.

The mental picture which we usually have of Adam and Eve in Eden is that of perfect adults, with wisdom and ability far beyond that which people have today. "An Aristotle was but the rubbish of an Adam, and Athens but the rudiments of Paradise," said one English poet. But Scripture does not tell us this much about the first human beings. Some of the early teachers of the church, such as St. Athanasius (in whose honor the "Athanasian Creed" is named), taught that human beings were created in a relatively immature state, with the promise of perfection in heaven if they continued obedient to God. They would even have been subject to a natural death, but not a death that is horror and chaos as it is after the Fall. The first sin, then, would have been a turning away from the *path* to perfection, rather than a fall from an already perfect state.

We can imagine that happening in the evolution of humanity. The first true woman and true man were aware that something greater than they was present, and that life and happiness were offered to them. But then, for some reason, at some time of life, it was easier to close eyes and ears to that and to turn away. Perhaps they met another tribe, almost like them, and knew that they were sisters and brothers—but it was easier, safer, to kill. Or perhaps they realized how beautiful they were, and how great it was to be able to think.

"You will be like God."

Perhaps it was like that. Somehow they turned away from God and refused to hear the Word—and, St. Athanasius says, when they turned from the Word, they turned toward nonbeing. The graves of early cave-dwellers, containing funerary gifts, suggest that they had a sense that something was terribly wrong when people died.

What happened then would have colored all of history—not just transmitting sin to the descendants of those first people, but giving a different meaning to the whole process of evolution that had taken place before. It's a little bit like the way in which the American Civil War colors our whole perception of what the voyages of Columbus and the Declaration of Independence really mean. (The idea that an event can affect things that happened before it may seem bizarre, but scientists today talk about the possibility of such things in the extreme realms of subatomic particles or black holes.)

That is one way in which we can try to talk about sin entering human history. There is another aspect of the traditional doctrine that can be considered as well. Genesis speaks of the serpent suggesting to Eve that she and her husband can be like God. There the serpent is only "more subtle than any other wild creature that the LORD God had made" (Gen. 3:1). But later, this began to be given a more cosmic significance. The temptation of humanity was associated with the idea of the rebellion of the angelic powers against God, something hinted at by Genesis 6:1-4 and Jude 6. The tempter was identified with Satan, the leader of the fallen angels.

> For God created man for incorruption, and made him in the image of his own eternity, but through the devil's envy death entered the world, and those who belong to his party experience it,

says the apocryphal Wisdom of Solomon (2:23-24). And Jesus speaks in a similar way to the Judeans who reject him:

> You are of your father the devil, and your will is to do your father's desires. He was a murderer from the beginning, and has nothing to do with the truth, because there is no truth in him. (Jn. 8:44)

And so, in the article "Of the Cause of Sin," the Augsburg Confession says simply,

> Our churches teach that although God creates and preserves nature, the cause of sin is the will of the wicked, that is, of the devil and ungodly people.

Associating the origin of evil with satanic powers can be dangerous, for it can encourage an unhealthy interest in the occult. More importantly, it may serve as an excuse for our own sinfulness

—"The devil made me do it." We need to remember that we are responsible for our own behavior.

On the other hand, this idea gives the problem of evil something of the cosmic scope which we instinctively feel it really has. Suffering, evil, sin, and death are not just things that human beings inflict upon themselves. Somehow, mysteriously, evil had been a problem before the earth existed, and poses a threat to the inhabitants of the galaxy in Andromeda—if there are any. We quickly enter the realm of science fiction. In fact, some literature of that type is perhaps best able to give us some sense of the scope and nature of evil in our scientific age. C.S. Lewis's "space trilogy" (*Out of the Silent Planet, Perelandra,* and *That Hideous Strength*) provides one example.

Of course, if we're going to speak of the devil, we need to get away from caricatures of grinning men with red long-johns and pitchforks. Evil is more fundamental than that sort of picture can suggest—"a structural fault in the universe" is the way that one theologian described the devil.

And there we come to a final way of talking about the presence of evil. Teilhard de Chardin, the paleontologist and theologian who spent much of his life trying to understand evolution in the Christian context, called evil the "shadow" of creation. God's creation of a universe which would develop toward the final state of full communion between creation and God meant also the possibility of creation turning *away* from God and toward nonbeing. Death, or the possibility of death, is there from the beginning of creation. That does not mean that evil and nonbeing are powers on the same level as God, as if there were an evil God as well as a good one. For God to be the creator means that he always defeats the powers of darkness and chaos that might swallow up creation.

Again, that is an idea which must be used with considerable care. It would be a serious error to suggest that evil is *some*thing which has existed since before creation. All things that exist were originally created good by God. The character of evil, as we said earlier, is precisely that it is *no*thing.

All of this talk of the origin of evil, of being and nonbeing, might sound like just an exercise for a philosophy class. We know that the matter is far more serious than that. The evening news forces the problem of evil to our attention, and most of us have had times of depression when the Deep seemed like the only "reality" that existed. Like the prophet Jeremiah, we feel that the universe is returning to the chaos that preceded the world:

> I looked on the earth, and lo, it was waste and void;
> and to the heavens, and they had no light.
> I looked on the mountains, and lo, they were quaking,
> and all the hills moved to and fro.
> I looked, and lo, there was no man,
> and all the birds of the air had fled.   (Jer. 4:23-25)

At those times, no scientific or theological speculation will do much good. Then it is a matter of life and death to know that the creator of the universe has come into the world as a creature, and has himself met abandonment and destruction in the darkness of Golgotha. Jesus cries out on the cross, "My God, my God, why have you forsaken me?" In his Incarnation, in his suffering, death, and burial, God has gone down into the Deep. We hold our breath, as if watching someone go into the raging waters to rescue a drowning person. But the one who disappears into the Deep is the one who creates out of nothing.

CHAPTER NINE

What Has Not Been Assumed Has Not Been Redeemed

"FOR US and for our salvation he came down from heaven," we say in the Nicene Creed. The Christian confession, and claim, and hope, is that the creator of the universe entered our history—that God became human:

> Creator of the stars of night,
> For us you veiled in flesh your light,
> And deigned our mortal form to wear,
> And shared our human want and care.
>
> (*Lutheran Book of Worship*, #101, v. 3)

The people of Israel saw God's action in their history—in events which actually took place, like the Exodus and the return from exile. And Jesus of Nazareth, the carpenter with dusty feet who sits down wearily beside the well at Sychar, is the stuff of which real history is made. In him, history reaches its climax. Jesus of Nazareth is God incarnate—God enfleshed.

In Jesus Christ, God saves, and redeems, and recreates humanity. Those different words we can use to describe this action —and certainly more could be listed—show its tremendous scope. There is no one way of looking at the work of Christ which does complete justice to it, for it is a work of cosmic significance. In Jesus Christ, God saves the entire universe. We discussed this in chapter 4, and now can look more deeply at the meaning of the Incarnation.

It is *God* who saves the world in Jesus Christ, we say. If this is the case, we ought to be able to see in the Incarnation what we have called the trademark of God, creation out of nothing. God brings hope and new life into situations in which all "sensible" human hope is gone. That is the sign which authenticates God's creative work.

"In those days a decree went out from Caesar Augustus. . . ." In the days when the Roman emperor ruled the Mediterranean world and was on his way to becoming a symbol of divinity, when the legions had put down all the revolts and the taxes flowed into the imperial city, Jesus was born in an outlying province—an occupied territory.

"Can anything good come out of Nazareth?" asked Nathanael when he heard where Jesus came from. Nazareth was the boondocks, the nowhere town that people made jokes about. The Temple of God was supposed to be in Jerusalem, adorned with all the gold and pagan splendor that Herod could get for it. For the pagans didn't know about creation out of nothing. . . .

But a finer impossibility comes when God's messenger is sent to a young peasant maiden in a nowhere village in a despised occupied territory of the empire of the world:

> "Don't be afraid, Mary; God has been gracious to you. You will become pregnant and give birth to a son, and you will name him Jesus. He will be great and will be called the Son of the Most High God." . . . Mary said to the angel, "I am a virgin. How, then, can this be?" The angel answered, "The Holy Spirit will come on you, and God's power will rest upon you. For this reason the holy child will be called the Son of God. . . . For there is nothing that God cannot do." (Lk. 1:29-37, TEV)

For Jesus to be conceived of a virgin is again creation out of nothing, hope where there was no hope. In earlier times, what would have seemed miraculous may have been a woman being able to bear a child without the active contribution of a man. The female was thought of as the "field" in which seed was sown. We know now, of course, that the female must contribute the egg and the male the sperm in order for conception to take place. But however we look at it, human conception by a virgin is an impossibility. And so from the first instant of life, the sign of God's new creation is placed upon Jesus:

> When you became man to set us free,
> you did not spurn the virgin's womb.   (from the *Te Deum*)

(God as a human embryo is a scandal, of course, an offense against our sense of what is "fitting." But God's sense of decorum must differ from ours. God is willing to become *very* small.)

Since, then, it is God who is present and active in Jesus, it is God who saves us and God to whom we owe our lives. It is this fundamental theme which lies behind all the centuries of debate about the divinity of Christ. "How could a human being actually be—*God*?" asks the skeptic. "Where in the Bible does Jesus actually say, in so many words, 'I am God'?" And if the discussion is carried on at that level, we can get a lot of exercise in philosophical debate or in checking proof-texts, and never really get anywhere. But that misses the point.

For it is Jesus Christ who saves us, and yet we are to look to God alone for life—"You shall have no other gods before me." If the one born in Bethlehem, the one who hangs on the cross, were not God, then we would be guilty of idolatry in looking to him as our savior. That is why, in spite of all questions about how it can be, in spite of all textual quibbles, the Christian church has always clung, as to a lifeline, to the confession that "in him the whole fulness of deity dwells bodily" (Col. 2:9). Only the creator can be the redeemer.

And yet, it is not *quite* accurate to say "Jesus is God." Jesus is *God Incarnate*, fully divine *and* fully human. It was necessary, the Letter to the Hebrews says, for him to be made like us in every way. And the church has had to struggle as hard to defend the full humanity of Christ as to uphold his divinity.

Why is that important? We've seen that Christ's divinity is

essential if we are to owe our life and being to God alone. But it is *our* life which is saved through the Incarnation. Our redemption is not accomplished by some masquerade, by God just pretending to be human. We would not be saved as whole people if God had not assumed everything that belongs to our full humanity.

Some of the statements of the theologians of the early church can be combined to give a very clear expression of this argument: What has not been assumed [that is, taken by God in the Incarnation] has not been redeemed. There is no way to stop short on our teaching about Christ's humanity without stopping short on our teaching about salvation.

This means that Jesus has a human mind and human understanding. His body is subject to all the joys and problems of human bodily existence. He has a human will, just as we do. And he also possesses in their fullness the divine understanding and will. There is one savior, possessing full humanity and full divinity. The classic statement of this, from the middle of the fifth century, says that Jesus Christ is "one *person* in two *natures.*"

As individual human beings, we can know then that God Incarnate has borne everything that we are, and has experienced everything that we have experienced, except that he has not sinned (Heb. 4:15). But the assumption of human nature by God is of even broader significance than that.

The human nature which is assumed in the Incarnation transcends the boundaries which we set up between human beings. The distinctions of social or economic class, of race or sex, are overcome in the person and work of Christ.

> There is neither Jew nor Greek,
> there is neither slave nor free,
> there is neither male nor female;
> for you are all one in Christ Jesus.   (Gal. 3:28)

Jesus of Nazareth was a Jew of the first century, biologically male, of a certain height and weight and with a certain color of skin. But the human nature which he bears is the nature which we all share, with what is essential to the humanness of blacks and whites and reds and browns and yellows, of women and men. "What has not been assumed has not been redeemed," and Jesus Christ, redeemer of the world, has assumed what is essential to the humanity of each of us.

For, properly speaking, Jesus is not *a* human being, though he is fully human. His humanity is the totality of human nature, which receives its personal, individual "centering" in the second person of the Trinity, the Word of God. There is one savior, one person, made known to us in two natures, human and divine.

It may seem odd to us to talk about an abstract "human nature" which is not tied down to *a* human being. This idea is unfamiliar to us partly because we tend to be individualists. Americans have an inborn suspicion of speaking about human beings as a collective, so that the idea of a common human nature doesn't mean a lot to us. In many other cultures, that has not been the case. "I am human, and nothing human is foreign to me," said the Roman poet Terence. And especially for the people of the Bible, our kind of individualism was hardly common.

For the people of Israel, there was a fundamental sharing of humanity between one person and another, between ancestor and descendant. We noticed in chapter 3 that *Adam* of Genesis 1 and 2 is the Hebrew word for "humanity"—for "man" in the older, generic sense. Thus when St. Paul says, "In Adam all die" in 1 Corinthians 15:22, he is saying something about what happened at the beginning of the human race *and* something about our common sharing in sin and death today. There is a real sense in which each of us is "included" in the other.

But Paul does more in that passage in 1 Corinthians than simply observe that we are all dying. "As in Adam all die, so also in Christ shall all be made alive." The definitive and saving "summing up" or "recapitulation" of the human race takes place in Jesus Christ. But he does not repeat our mistakes. Jesus does right what we failed to do, and does it on our behalf.

There is the fascinatingly brief account of Jesus's temptation in Mark 1:13. "And he was in the wilderness forty days, tempted

by Satan; and he was with the wild beasts; and the angels minis-
tered to him." "He was with the wild beasts," just as Adam was
in Paradise with the animals, and gave names to them. But
humanity in Jesus does not yield to the voice of Satan, the voice
of the tempter, as Adam and Eve yielded. Jesus "does it right the
second time around."

(It is interesting to note what the gospels of Matthew and Luke
have done in expanding and changing this simple account without
altering the basic theme of "doing it right the second time around."
In Matthew 4:1-11, the devil offers Jesus three temptations—to
put food ahead of God, to put God to the test, and to worship
someone other than God. These are the same temptations that
Israel succumbed to during *its* wandering in the wilderness—Israel
which is described as the Lord's "first-born son" [Ex. 4:22]. But
Jesus, the Son of God, does not yield to these temptations.)

Our lives as individuals, as well as the history of Israel, are
also "summed up" in Christ. The early teachers of the church
pointed out that the human birth and conception and growth to
maturity of God Incarnate (as, for example, in Luke 2:52) meant
that all the stages of our life, infant and youth and adult, are shared
in and are taken up into the life of God. As we look toward the
end of life, we see that Christ shares also our death. And because
he has taken our humanity, never to be separated from it, we are
also to become sharers in his resurrection.

When we go back in the other direction, toward the beginnings
of life, we also see something fascinating and very relevant to our
study of evolution. Those who study the development of the
embryo have long recognized that there are relationships between
the way that human beings develop in the womb and the evolutionary history of the human race. At corresponding stages of
development, the human embryo shows a great similarity to the
embryos of our relatives in evolutionary development. It is almost
as if, up to a certain stage of development, we all had to cover
the same stages of development.

We know too that it is not only in our development in the

womb that these relationships show themselves. Our chemical make-up is closely related to that of other mammals, and the "genetic code" which allows our cells to transmit the information needed to copy themselves is the same code "spoken" by all the other organisms on earth. We carry about in our bodies the marks of our relationship to all the rest of God's creation.

This means that, in the Incarnation, God has united himself not merely to humanity, but to the whole creation. It was necessary for him to do this in order to save the whole creation, as is promised in Romans 8:18-25. "God, the Son, redeemer of the world, have mercy on us," sings the litany.

In fact, we can argue that evolution, with its close links between all creatures on earth, is almost a theological necessity. Scripture testifies clearly to God's purpose to redeem the whole creation, to make a new heaven and a new earth. Not only human beings, but horses and cacti and saber-toothed tigers are, in some sense, to be saved. But "what has not been assumed has not been redeemed." God does not save by some arbitrary decree, but by taking to himself that which he would redeem and make immortal. In order to save all creatures, he must take all creatures to himself. If humanity were a special creation, separate from other creatures, this assumption of other creatures could not have been accomplished by God becoming human. But evolution has shown us that human nature is closely linked with the natures of all creatures. By taking on human nature, God took all creatures to himself. If scientists had not discovered evolution, theologians should have! (And, as we saw in chapter 3, some came very close to doing so.)

The Incarnation of the Word of God is what "makes it all work." The creator of the universe became a creature in order to save the fallen world and unite it to himself. But we have not yet reached the center of this mystery:

> He became incarnate from the virgin Mary, and was made man.
> For our sake he was crucified under Pontius Pilate;
> he suffered death and was buried.

God's act in the Incarnation bears the trademark of all his work, the sign of creation out of nothing. From the beginning it was stamped on our universe like some cryptic, half-understood symbol. And now we come to see that the trademark of God's work is the sign of the cross.

CHAPTER TEN

"The Dust of Death"

To LIFT A HEAVY LOAD, you have to get under it—all the way under. And so when God would raise up the whole fallen world, the first act was one of descent:

> Therefore it is said,
> "When he ascended on high he led a host of captives,
>   and he gave gifts to men."
> (In saying, "He ascended," what does it mean but that he had also descended into the lower parts of the earth? He who descended is he who also ascended far above all the heavens, that he might fill all things.) (Eph. 4:8-10)

The descent of God is no halfway measure. "He came down from heaven"—for to become Incarnate in our sinful world was an act of condescension. But he keeps on going down—into the depths, into the ghostly common grave and underworld that the Israelites called Sheol and the Pit, into Hell itself.

God has put his mark on human history before this. In the Exodus and the return from exile there were destruction and nothingness, and then new life. God created out of nothing. But those works were not complete. There was real enough resurrection, but resurrection of the dead only in a symbolic sense. The Israelites who died in exile in Babylon left their bones there, and never again saw Jerusalem. In Ezekiel's vision of the valley of dry bones, those lifeless remains represent the nation of Israel which would be resurrected, though individual members had died.

> Then he said to me, "Son of man, these bones are the whole house of Israel. Behold, they say, 'Our bones are dried up, and our hope is lost; we are clean cut off.' Therefore prophesy, and say to them, Thus says the Lord GOD: Behold, I will open your graves, and raise you from your graves, O my people; and I will bring you home into the land of Israel. And you shall know that I am the LORD, when I open your graves, and raise you from your graves, O my people." (Ez. 37:11-13)

Israel did return from exile, and the nation was remade. The Jews thought that the prophecy had been fulfilled. But God promises more than we expect. There is a hint of that even in Ezekiel's vision—not only the scattered and withered exiles of Israel, but those who lie in the graves.

For death is something that cries out for salvation. Death is the final abandonment, the final loss of importance and meaning for our lives.

"My God, my God, why hast thou forsaken me?" cried out one of Israel's psalmists:

> Why art thou so far from helping me, from the words of my
>   groaning?
>
> . . . .
>
> But I am a worm, and no man;
> scorned by men, and despised by the people.
>
> . . . .
>
> My strength is dried up like a potsherd,
> and my tongue cleaves to my jaws;
> thou dost lay me in the dust of death.   (Ps. 22:1, 6, 15)

There is no point in pretending that death doesn't matter. Joseph Conrad's Kurtz, who cries out, "The horror! The horror!" as he lies waiting for death in *Heart of Darkness*, speaks for all of us. Death destroys the meaning of my life for *me*. And while my memory and influence may live on, the extinction of the human race and the heat death of the universe will finally destroy all meaning. Our ideas of progress and purpose finally must face reality and die too.

All of us die, and all could cry out, "My God, my God, why hast thou forsaken me?" But we know one of us who did cry that, and that one was God Incarnate. He is in the darkness where God cannot find God. For Jesus, who is the light of the world, it is horror to be shrouded in that darkness. "My soul is very sorrowful, even to death," he tells his disciples in Gethsemane.

"You have laid me in the dust of death." Can even God *bring back* that which is dead? What hope is there for our fond experiences, our lost friends, dead lovers and extinct species? How can there be any meaning to our existence, any vindication of the struggles of our lives, if all those things that make our lives meaningful are gone? We know the old theories about the origin of the universe, and the old stories about the Red Sea and Babylon —but can God *really* create out of nothing?

Creation itself mourns the death of its creator. One of the afternoon prayers of the Eastern Church imagines the thought of a thief crucified with Jesus:

> The sight of life's very source suspended on the cross made the thief cry out: "If this man who hangs with us were not God, the sun would never hide its light, nor would the earth so quake and tremble!"

Yet this one who hangs in darkness is the one who remakes the world, "who for the joy that was set before him endured the cross, despising the shame, and is seated at the right hand of the throne of God" (Heb. 12:2). The cross is God's victory over death, his most stunning and surprising act of divine creation out of nothing. The cross and resurrection of Christ are inextricably linked as the masterpiece of all God's work.

The dead Christ lies in the tomb—and the dead do not rise. Just as the "waste and void" and the "Deep" of Genesis meant the impossibility of existence for the universe, so the cross, in human terms, means the impossibility of the life of Christ. It is not as if the Deep or the dead had some kind of potential to become something—as if they just had to try hard. There is nothing to try. All that lies between the Deep and the universe is the power of God. All that lies between Good Friday and Easter is the power of God. And Christ *is* risen, and the world is made new.

> But in fact Christ has been raised from the dead, the first fruits of those who have fallen asleep. For as by a man came death, by a man has also come the resurrection of the dead. For as in Adam all die, so also in Christ shall all be made alive. (1 Cor. 15:20-22)

It would be presumptuous for us to think that we understand completely *how* the cross and resurrection of Christ have recreated the world. Creation out of nothing is always beyond our ability to grasp and comprehend. But we can see again that this work bears the sign that we have come to associate with the work of God. The creator has descended to the very depths of the world to lift up its whole weight and burden.

The incredible, absurd hope that the dead Christ could live has been fulfilled. Our most extravagant hopes may be accomplished by the power of God. (It will be the small, fearful hopes that fail. Evolution will not restore the dinosaurs and mastodons, but something new will come out of extinction. We will not have peace if we hope in our horses and chariots and nuclear missiles, but we may if we trust in something less "sensible." Perhaps instead of hoping for a balance of terror we should hope for peace.)

Christ is not restored to life just as he was before, but he is still the crucified one. The risen Christ still bears the marks of nails and spear (Jn. 20:24-29)—he wears them as medals won on the battlefield. And yet he is not the same—his close friends don't recognize him (Lk. 24:16, Jn. 20:14). Walls and locks have no power to exclude his body, which seems now to be in a quite different relation to space and time. But still—he makes a point of eating with his disciples (Lk. 24:41-43).

This is resurrection of the body, but of a body transformed from the condition that we know.

But someone will ask, "How are the dead raised? With what kind of body do they come?" You foolish man! What you sow does not come to life unless it dies. And what you sow is not the body which is to be, but a bare kernel, perhaps of wheat or of some other grain. But God gives it a body as he has chosen, and to each kind of seed its own body. . . . So is it with the resurrection of the dead. What is sown is perishable, what is raised is imperishable. It is sown in dishonor, it is raised in glory. It is sown in weakness, it is raised in power. It is sown a physical body, it is raised a spiritual body. (1 Cor. 15:35-38, 42-44)

Christ in his resurrection body is raised to "the right hand of God." God's "right hand" is a symbol of his almighty power, and the risen lord Jesus is invested with that divine power over the whole universe. "All authority in heaven and on earth has been given to me" (Mt. 28:18), he tells his disciples. "God's right hand is everywhere," said Martin Luther. God rules the universe by his immediate presence, not as an absentee landlord. He is in direct relationship with everything in the universe. And the risen Christ, the one who was crucified, shares in that rule according to his humanity because of the personal union of the human and divine natures. Jesus rules in heaven, but he is present on earth with the church, which is his body.

Because God has taken human nature to himself in the Incarnation, our human nature has been put to death on the cross. Our baptism is a participation in this death and burial, as St. Paul teaches in Romans 6:3-11. And human nature has been raised with Christ, and we also share in that through baptism. In the resurrection, the Lord of space and time has become the head of a new humanity which no longer needs to be in fear of death. Christ our head has passed beyond that. "Christ being raised from the dead will never die again; death no longer has dominion over him" (Rom. 6:9).

Since Christ is the Lord of space and time, the immensities of the universe and the unknown stretches of past and future no longer have to terrify us. A human being with the same nature as ours, the nature to which it was said, "You are dust, and to dust you shall return," rules over the galaxies. When we remember the billions of years of history of the universe and of the earth, it is only yesterday that the resurrection of Christ took place. And now we are beginning to understand the secrets of the universe, instead of just making up stories about them.

Battles between good and evil are still going on—but the war has already been decided. It's as in World War II, when the power behind the death camps was really broken on D-Day. But people continued to die for a time.

We naturally want to begin our story with the origin of the world. The Bible begins with the creation accounts of Genesis, and we feel that our scientific accounts of things are most orderly if we can tie them in with the origin of life or with the Big Bang. But in order to see the course of the world's history most clearly, it's necessary to view it from the standpoint of the cross and resurrection of Jesus. These stand together at the center of the world. At Golgotha we see clearly the sign which God has placed on the universe from the beginning, the sign of the cross. From Golgotha we see the end of the world, when all will share openly in the power of the resurrection. There is a note in Matthew's gospel which suggests that this is already happening. When Jesus died on the cross,

> the tombs also were opened, and many bodies of the saints who had fallen asleep were raised, and coming out of the tombs after his resurrection they went into the holy city and appeared to many. (Mt. 27:52-53)

That kind of story can easily make a person feel skeptical. Did it really happen? Did a lot of dead people—not just one, but "many"—rise from their graves and walk around in Jerusalem? Isn't that just a poetic way of saying that the power of death is destroyed, and that we are to share in Christ's resurrection?

Perhaps so—though the defeat of death is not "just" anything. It is a tremendous fact for which any imagery—the opening of the tombs of Jerusalem or the enlivening of the dry bones—is inadequate. The accounts of the resurrection of Christ in the four Gospels are difficult to harmonize if they are treated strictly as historical records, like the court testimonies of four witnesses. What happened is too big and too awesome to be tied down in that way. It's significant that none of the biblical accounts try to describe the actual moment of resurrection. (And some of the most disappointing paintings are ones which attempt to show this event. How could anyone come close to doing it justice?) Our minds are tied to what exists, and are not well suited to grasp how reality can be brought from impossibility, and the living one from death.

The resurrection can't be enclosed and bound within the confines of the history of our physical world, yet it was something historical. Jesus was "crucified under Pontius Pilate"—a man we know from secular history, like Julius Caesar. And St. Paul, in his first letter to the Corinthians, thinks it important to list the witnesses of Christ's resurrection. To confess the resurrection is an act of faith, but faith in something which actually happened and which affects our lives.

In the creation account of Genesis 2, God creates humanity out of the dust of the earth. We have seen that that corresponds nicely with what science has to say about us. We are made of earthly material, and we will go back to the dust. But God's work does not end there. The creator has himself come down into the dust to save humanity. Through the resurrection of the dead, God gives meaning to the everyday activities that make up our lives. Not just our bodies, but our lives, are to be raised and glorified.

We're used to thinking of the meaning of Christ's death and resurrection in other ways. We may say that Christ died to pay the penalty for our sin against God, so that whoever believes in him may receive forgiveness. The emphasis is then on God's declaration of our righteousness for the sake of the death and resurrection of Christ. That is a different way of speaking about the death and resurrection of Christ, though not at all one that contradicts our emphasis on the renewal of creation. For God's declaration that we are righteous is not an empty promise or some sort of legal fiction. God's word *creates*, just as it created in the beginning. (We see that even in human relationships. When someone we trust promises to do something, we feel that "it's as good as done.") And so God's declaration that a sinner is righteous is an act of creation and renewal.

God declares us righteous, but we know only too well that we will have trouble finding "proofs" of our righteousness that would be convincing to the world. Often we don't even seem very righteous to ourselves! It's the same kind of difficulty that we have in trying to find any overwhelming "proofs" of the resurrection. In fact, those two things are linked. The resurrection life of believers is hidden.

> If then you have been raised with Christ, seek the things that are above, where Christ is, seated at the right hand of God. Set your minds on things that are above, not on things that are on earth. For you have died, and your life is hid with Christ in God. When Christ who is our life appears, then you also will appear with him in glory. (Col. 3:1-4)

Righteousness and the resurrection life are hidden, but they aren't sealed away in some kind of cosmic safety deposit box. Through the power of the Holy Spirit, they become effective in our lives. The life and righteousness which God creates in us are probably more apparent to others than to us, for they are to be used in the service of others. God has made us for life. How then are we to live as God's new creation?

CHAPTER ELEVEN

Evolutionary Ethics

So—HOW ARE WE TO LIVE? We don't find ourselves alone in a meaningless universe, with no idea of how we got here. The triune God has created a good world, and has made the human race in the image of the Holy Trinity. We have evolved from the simplest forms of life—even from nonliving matter—to be able to contemplate and to understand our origins, and to respond to the call of God. We have turned away from the road that leads to God, but God in Jesus Christ has taken our nature to find us and to bring us back to God. The new creation is begun, a creation in which we are called to be active. And how are we to act?

We are tightly connected with the rest of the living world, and with the whole universe, by a complex web of relationships. We are descended from what we call the "lower animals"—from long-extinct creatures whose lives were concerned with surviving, getting food, and reproducing. Human nature has evolved.

That is one aspect of how we got here and what we are. We need to remember that part of the story when we think about our moral responsibilities and opportunities in the world. Realistic ethical decisions must take account of what we are. We simply fool ourselves if we think of human beings as unfallen angels.

But evolution is not the whole story. We have emphasized all along that evolution is not an *alternative* to creation. To say that we have evolved is not to do away with the teaching that we are creatures of God, called to do God's will. Evolution is the process through which God has created us.

Evolutionary theory tells us something about what we have been and what we are. It does not tell us what we are called to be. The Christian doctrine of creation says that we owe our lives to God, who has created us in his image, putting us over the rest of creation as his representatives and stewards:

> Thou hast given him dominion over the works of thy hands;
> thou hast put all things under his feet. (Ps. 8:6)

We can get pretty cynical about that without even trying very hard. So we're created in the image of God—but we certainly don't act like it. It seems as if the rest of the world could get along fine without our bungling attempts to exercise dominion over it.

It's true that, if we had to rely on our own dignity or worth or accomplishments, we'd present a pretty sorry sight to the universe. And the core of the Christian message is that we *don't* have to rely on those things. In Christ, God the creator has saved us, renewed us in the image of God, and brought new life to the world. The ways of destruction and death, though God has been able to make use of them in creation, don't have to hold our allegiance. We share the animal nature of the wild beasts. And because of the Incarnation, we may "become partakers of the divine nature" (2 Pet. 1:4).

The way we have come, what we are, and what we have been called to be—all of those have to be taken into account. Only in that way can we respond realistically and hopefully to the world we share.

Our temptation is to seek the old, familiar paths and structures of life. The political framework, the social organization, and the religious practices that we and our parents have been familiar with are the ones we long for. It seems always to have been that way. Even after his resurrection, Jesus's disciples expected him to "restore the kingdom to Israel" (Acts 1:6). They still didn't look for God to do something really new.

Some of the patterns followed by human evolution have the same appeal. We have to be especially on the lookout for these, because there is a tendency to regard these patterns as unchangeable aspects of human nature. But these patterns may be simply survival tactics which had a limited usefulness in the past but which are no longer helpful.

National and racial exclusiveness is one such pattern. In one rather limited sense, what evolution does is to preserve and pass on (with slow modifications) the hereditary characteristics of a population. A tribe made up of people who were closely related could protect its own genetic information which produced its hereditary characteristics from any mixing by refusing to breed with people too different from it. Fighting to defend or extend its own territory could serve the same end. Ethnic groups that survived as well-defined units were those that somehow isolated themselves from interbreeding with other groups. To a certain extent, "master race" theories and racial segregation continue survival patterns which many groups have used in the past.

"In the past"—those are the words to notice. In the long run, to survive and to thrive requires not the repetition of old patterns but adaptation to new environments and situations. To continue old patterns in new situations has often led to the extinction of species.

And it is clear that, in the present situation of the world, a narrow tribalism is almost a guarantee of extinction. We have realized in the United States that racial segregation produces intolerable tensions in society today. And technology has reached the point where war to defend or extend boundaries has the potential to destroy all nations. It's significant that the last major nation to try to establish the rule of a "master race," Nazi Germany, began a war which not only leveled it, but introduced the nuclear weapons which can destroy all humanity.

People have tried to uphold tribal and racial "purity" for thousands of years, and the people of the Bible were often no exception. But it is interesting to note the attitude of the Old Testament on the matter. When the Jews were reduced to a tiny, threatened minority after their return from exile, prohibitions against marriages with foreigners were enforced (for example, Neh. 13:23-30). In an earlier day the Israelites seem to have been freer about this. Ruth, the ancestor of King David and of Christ, was a Moabite woman. From the beginning there was in Israel a seed of the idea that all nations and tribes and peoples and tongues (Rev. 7:9) are to be included in the people of God.

Distinction between the sexes has also been connected with our evolutionary development. This is hardly surprising, for there are real differences in biological functions between men and women. There is considerable debate today about how such things as the subordination of women, which has been quite common in our culture until recently, developed. "Traditional" and "feminist" anthropologists may come to quite different conclusions about that.

One argument is that the close tie between mother and child for some time after birth would keep adult women out of some more adventurous activities, such as hunting, for significant periods of time. In tribes of hunters and gatherers (as humans were before the discovery of agriculture around ten thousand years ago), being excluded from hunting would mean that one of the more prestigious roles would be closed to women. This would be reinforced by some physical differences between men and women. Our large brains are essential to our humanity. But in order to give birth to babies with large heads, women have to have a pelvic structure which keeps them from running as fast as men.

That may explain how the subordination of women began. We cannot be certain of that, and some scientists would argue that the early stages of development of human culture were shaped by women. (We might ask, for example, who discovered agriculture if men were doing the hunting!) In any case, the subordination of women did develop, and played some role in our evolution. That needs to be recognized—but not clung to. Hunting and running are not essentials for survival today, and there is no longer any evolutionary value in sexual subordination. In fact, it seems impossible for this sort of subordination to be maintained in the kind of evolution which Christianity envisions. There, people are called upon to develop greater openness and closer relationships with one another.

It is worth noting that, just as with race, the Old Testament tends to break down some of the sexual stereotypes which have been with us for so long. There is, of course, a good deal of material in the Old Testament which treats women as inferior human beings. For example, a woman was considered unclean for forty days after giving birth to a male, but for eighty if she had a female child (Lev. 12:1-5). But one of the early heroes of Israel is the judge Deborah (Jg. 4, 5). It is a woman whose judgment is appealed to in a time of crisis for Judah, the prophet Huldah (2 Kg. 22:11-20). Thus the history of Israel drives toward the practice and teaching of Jesus, in which women are treated without regard for any supposed inferiority. In Christ, that is done away with.

> There is neither Jew nor Greek, there is neither slave nor free, there is neither male nor female; for you are all one in Christ Jesus. (Gal. 3:28)

In Christ there is a radical change in the process of evolution. Other such changes have taken place in the history of the earth—when life arose, and when life became conscious of itself in humanity. The gradual character of evolution does not rule out abrupt changes, as an example from another area of science will illustrate. Though the temperature of a substance may be varied quite slowly, there are critical temperatures at which marked qualitative changes like melting and boiling take place. Ice and water and steam are simply not the same. So, perhaps, we may imagine evolution to take place. With the coming of Christ and the grafting of the divine nature into the human race, the old evolutionary patterns of competition and combat begin to become obsolete. The "shadow of creation" which we spoke of in chapter 8 becomes smaller and smaller.

To ignore the need of another man or woman is to diminish one's own humanity. That was true in the distant past as well, but we only see that in the light of the Incarnation.

When the Son of man comes in his glory, and all the angels with him, then he will sit on his glorious throne. Before him will be gathered all the nations, and he will separate them one from another as a shepherd separates the sheep from the goats, and he will place the sheep at his right hand, but the goats at the left. Then the King will say to those at his right hand, "Come, O blessed of my Father, inherit the kingdom prepared for you from the foundation of the world; for I was hungry and you gave me food, I was thirsty and you gave me drink, I was a stranger and you welcomed me, I was naked and you clothed me, I was sick and you visited me, I was in prison and you came to me." Then the righteous will answer him, "Lord, when did we see thee hungry and feed thee, or thirsty and give thee drink? And when did we see thee a stranger and welcome thee, or naked and clothe thee? And when did we see thee sick or in prison and visit thee?" And the King will answer them, "Truly, I say to you, as you did it to one of the least of these my brethren, you did it to me." (Mt. 25:31-40)

But to those who failed to respond to the needs of others, the King says, "Depart from me, you cursed" (Mt. 25:41). To appeal to "survival of the fittest" to justify one's selfishness is to fight against God's Christ.

All of this may sound as if our nature as creatures who have evolved is something entirely negative which has to be overcome by God. But evolution also has some positive things to say about the way we should live in the world.

One of the most fundamental things that evolutionary theory teaches us is our profound unity with the rest of creation. We are made of atoms formed in the furnaces of the stars, and the seas in which our ancestors swam flow through our veins. The universe is a place made for us to live in, not a place for us to escape from.

That relationship with the whole universe is not something that belongs only to our history. We have learned at considerable cost during the past decades that our relationship with the environment requires our responsible attention. "Let them have dominion" is not a license to use the world just as a source of raw materials or as a sewer. Relationships are two-way things. If we poison the environment, we soon find that we've poisoned our own air and water and food. Our responsibility to other human beings, if nothing else, would require that we care for the common environment.

While we recognize that we do participate in the whole universe, it is our kinship with the rest of the human race which will draw our most immediate ethical concern. That is not something that we had to wait for evolution to teach us. The idea, based on an interpretation of the Genesis creation accounts as literal history, that we are all descended from Adam and Eve, would also mean that we were all distant cousins of one another. The unity of the human race has always been an important part of Christian tradition.

That unity is a present reality because it is embodied in Christ, who is the head of a new humanity and the center of the new creation. As we do unto one of the least of Christ's brothers and sisters, we do unto God Incarnate. "He who has once realized the fact that God was made man cannot speak and act inhumanly," said Karl Barth.

When we let the Incarnation illumine ethical problems, we may see things that we neglected before. The issue of abortion, for example, has often focused on the question of when a fetus can be considered a living human being. It is possible to deal with that question in different ways. But in any case, the Word of God was incarnate in the womb of Mary from the first moment of conception. There was never an instant when what was borne by her was not personally united with the divine nature. (The Feast of the Annunciation on March 25th, nine months before Christmas, is the celebration of the Incarnation.) A human fetus is capable of receiving the divine nature.

In fact, the full evolutionary vision of the Incarnation is that all creatures are somehow to be taken up into the new creation. The question of human responsibility to other animals often has not been taken seriously, in part because of the belief that humans and animals are completely different kinds of creatures. Evolution makes it difficult to hold that view. We at least have to consider the issue of "animal rights," for which some people have argued recently. It would be impractical, to say the least, to insist that other animals have the same rights that humans do. (Dogs and cats and horses appeal to our sympathy. Rats and flies don't.) But there is some value in thinking about the matter. A society that worried a bit about animals' right to life would be less likely to try to justify the murder of members of our own species!

Evolution isn't just something that *has* happened. It *is* happening, moving forward into God's future. The call of God which informs our ethical responses points us toward the convergence of all creation on Christ. Our response to situations must change as the world changes. Evolution helps us get used to that. But everything does not change, for the same Christ continues to be present for us. We may always ask if our actions will help to build up the body of Christ, and so move toward the fulfillment of God's new creation. And so when the bread and wine are brought for the Eucharist, the Lutheran liturgy has the prayer:

> Blessed are you, O Lord our God, maker of all things. Through your goodness you have blessed us with these gifts. With them we offer ourselves to your service and dedicate our lives to the care and redemption of all that you have made, for the sake of him who gave himself for us, Jesus Christ our Lord. Amen. (*LBW*, p. 68)

CHAPTER TWELVE

"Unto the Ages of Ages"

I am the Alpha and the Omega. . . . I am the first and the last, and the living one; I died, and behold I am alive for evermore, and I have the keys of Death and Hades. (Rev. 1:8, 17, 18)

So the risen and glorified Christ speaks to the seer at the beginning of the Book of Revelation. Alpha and omega—the first and last letters of the Greek alphabet. It is as if Christ were to say that he is the A and the Z of the universe, the beginning and the end. It is from this phrase that Teilhard de Chardin, the Jesuit priest and student of evolution, took the term which he used for the final goal of the evolution of the universe—"The Omega Point." The entire course of the universe converges on Christ.

Converges—that's a key word. Evolution isn't just a spreading out of the tree of life, with the development of more and more different organisms. The Incarnation makes a fundamental difference, for because of it, there is a *coming together* of life and the universe in Christ.

Questions about the next stage of evolution can provoke almost endless debate or fantasy. One extreme possibility is the extinction of the human race through ecological disaster or nuclear suicide. It is unfortunate that we do have to take such possibilities seriously. On the other hand, we can find science fiction visions of the far future in which human beings have evolved into strange shapes or into pure brains. And we might wonder if becoming nothing but minds wouldn't be just a more subtle form of extinction.

Where is human evolution going? The biblical vision insists on hope, even in the apparently hopeless situations which the six o'clock news sometimes presents us with. But that hope is for something *new*—not just for things continuing according to the same old patterns. The God who creates out of nothing is the God who surprises. Perhaps we're not being as imaginative as we should be—as imaginative as both science and Scripture ask us to be.

First, we should note that the use of *tools* by human beings represents a radical change in evolution. Very primitive tools simply give an extension of human capabilities: a club lets a person's reach be extended a little, and allows a heavier blow to be struck. But we have now reached a point where our tools enable us to do things which we couldn't do at all without them. It's safe to predict that humans will never evolve wings like birds, but our technological evolution gives us the ability to fly anyway. We can "see" the invisible with no changes in our "real" eyes, and are free from smallpox without having developed any "natural" immunity. Our use of tools has helped to put us at least partially in charge of our own evolution. "Genetic engineering," with its possibilities for deliberate modification of human heredity, gives the clearest example of this.

Let's also remember that the process of evolution has not just involved systems getting bigger and bigger. Instead, there have been changes in the *kinds* of systems which exist. When a system gets complex enough, its whole *character* may change.

When the earth was young, it was covered with quite simple molecules. The planet appeared dead, for water and carbon dioxide and ammonia and so forth don't in themselves show any signs of life. But soon the remarkable ability of carbon to form large, complex molecules began to show itself. When these molecules became large enough, the ability to reproduce and "do things" appeared. Life emerged. The whole is more than just the sum of its parts, as an ant colony is more than just thousands of individual ants, and a human brain more than millions of cells. Life is a result of complex organization.

And these large living molecules again did something new. They were gathered together to form a new type of structure, the cell. For hundreds of millions of years, one-celled animals were the earth's most advanced life forms. But again, cells didn't just get bigger and bigger. Multicelled creatures emerged, and evolved, finally reaching the stage of human beings. And now . . . ?

Teilhard de Chardin pointed out that, if we observe the recent course of human history, we can see another significant act of grouping taking place almost before our eyes. The main thrust of human evolution doesn't seem to be primarily in the direction of further changes in *individual* men and women. (There are probably no humans today with more native ability than Aristotle or the author of the Book of Job. And much of the improvement in human health or stature or athletic performance can be traced to improved nutrition or preventive medicine rather than to any genetic changes.) Humanity seems to be evolving in the direction of greater *cooperation.*

It may seem naive to say that, with all the quarrels and competitiveness and "rumors of wars" in the world today. But we have to look beneath the surface. Even that most threatening of our developments, nuclear weaponry, illustrates this new degree of human cooperation. There's no way that the atomic bomb could have been developed by an individual, though there were many important individual contributions. Instead, this discovery was the result of the cooperation of thousands of men and women who put their minds and talents together toward a common goal. This is only one example of the way in which modern research operates. The same kind of thing is seen in putting people on the moon or developing new treatments for cancer.

(The atomic bomb seems like an unfortunate example of human cooperation. Surely a world bristling with nuclear weapons isn't *progress!* Sin, the turning away from God which results in hatred for our neighbors, taints all of our activities. Just as we can turn our individual gifts in evil directions, we can turn cooperation toward destructive ends. Technical and moral progress simply don't always go together, as the story of the Tower of Babel shows.)

The importance of cooperation also shows itself in a change in the *mechanism* of evolution. We've seen that, in prehuman evolution, there is no "transmission of acquired characteristics." The giraffe doesn't pass on the longer neck which it gets by stretching to reach the top branches. But with our cultural evolution, there certainly is a process by which acquired characteristics are passed on to the next generation—education.

We transmit the things we learn—our art, our insights into human nature and the character of reality, and our discoveries and inventions. In spite of the fact that there may never have been a greater scientific mind than Einstein's, college students today may know more about relativity than he did because they can pick up where he left off. Each generation doesn't have to start from scratch, but can avoid the time-consuming false starts our mothers and fathers had to make and the misconceptions that geniuses of the past have freed us from. (Though we can always refuse to learn from the past, and continue to repeat its mistakes.) We all stand on the shoulders of giants.

The convergence of human evolution can suggest unappealing pictures—the termite colony or the collectivized states of this century which have tried to crush human personality under the load of Nazi or communist ideology. If the ant-heap society is the "wave of the future," few of us want any part of it. To have our persons melted down into an undifferentiated mass, like those sad families which are so bound together that their members have no separate identities, is a prospect as dismal as that of nuclear war.

But at that earlier stage of evolution, when multicelled organisms developed, progress was not made by a melting down of individual cells into one super-cell. Instead, creatures with distinct members and organs developed, having parts that couldn't simply be interchanged for one another. Head and stomach and lung and foot are part of a united whole, for they can't make it on their own. And they can't take over each other's roles either. All of the members are essential for the proper working of the body.

"Now there are varieties of gifts, but the same Spirit"; St. Paul tells the Corinthians,

> And there are varieties of service, but the same Lord; and there are varieties of working, but it is the same God who inspires them all in every one. To each is given the manifestation of the Spirit for the common good. . . .
>
> For just as the body is one and has many members, and all the members of the body, though many, are one body, so it is with Christ. For by one Spirit we were all baptized into one body—Jews or Greeks, slaves or free—and all were made to drink of one Spirit.
>
> For the body does not consist of one member but of many. If the foot should say, "Because I am not a hand, I do not belong to the body," that would not make it any less a part of the body. And if the ear should say, "Because I am not an eye, I do not belong to the body," that would not make it any less a part of the body. If the whole body were an eye, where would be the hearing? If the whole body were an ear, where would be the sense of smell? But as it is, God arranged the organs in the body, each one of them, as he chose. If all were a single organ, where would the body be? As it is, there are many parts, yet one body. . . . If one member suffers, all suffer together; if one member is honored, all rejoice together.
>
> Now you are the body of Christ and individually members of it. (1 Cor. 12:4-7, 12-20, 26-27)

This realization that the church, the whole community of Christians, is the "body of Christ," is one of the great insights of St. Paul. It was an insight that he was given on the Damascus road when he saw that, in persecuting Christians, he was persecuting the Christ who reigns in heavenly glory (Acts 9:3-5).

God took up and "enpersoned" our whole human nature in the Incarnation, and raised it up beyond death in the descent and reascent of Good Friday and Easter. Through these saving acts, which bear the unmistakable trademark of God's work, Christ has become the head of a new humanity. He is the source of the new creation.

All who belong to Christ are one body, one organism. The personal character and uniqueness of each are preserved, but we are united into one living reality whose head is Christ. Indeed, we are most truly ourselves when we are united with our brothers and sisters, and can use our talents and gifts to the full. We may remember meeting someone who at first seemed dull and uninteresting, but who seemed almost literally to "come alive" when she was with family or friends, with people who would share love and trust. "I saw a completely different side of her," we say, and perhaps we then most saw that person as she was meant to be.

The church is the living body of Christ. It is supplied with the very life of God, for it is fed with the body and blood of Christ:

> For no man ever hates his own flesh, but nourishes and cherishes it, as Christ does the church, because we are members of his body. (Eph. 5:29-30)

Because the church receives the body of Christ in the Eucharist, it *is* the body of Christ. And because the church is the Lord's body, the meal which it celebrates is the Lord's Supper.

The Eucharist is a holy communion of believers with their Lord and with one another. It is also our communion with the universe, and with the whole life of the world. It is through bread and wine—through matter, through the basic stuff that fuels our bodies and of which our bodies are made—that the life of God comes to us. But there is even more. The elements of the Eucharist are not bare grain and grapes, but those things with human invention and labor added, bread and wine—"fruit of the vine and work of human hands." God communes with us in the things which bind us closely to nature, yet which also mark us out as the image of God.

So the church, the body of Christ whose head is the crucified and risen Lord, is intimately linked with all of creation. It is, in fact, the center of the new creation, the means through which God remakes the world. The church, which is marked with the sign of the cross, is the nucleus and the pattern for the convergence of the whole world in Christ.

> He is the image of the invisible God, the first-born of all creation; for in him all things were created, in heaven and on earth, visible and invisible, whether thrones or dominions or principalities or authorities—all things were created through him and for him. He is before all things, and in him all things hold together. He is the head of the body, the church; he is the beginning, the first-born from the dead, that in everything he might be pre-eminent. For in him all the fulness of God was pleased to dwell, and through him to reconcile to himself all things, whether on earth or in heaven, making peace by the blood of his cross. (Col. 1:15-20)

"To reconcile to himself all things." God took on human nature to redeem it. And because humanity carries links of many kinds, embryological, structural, genetic and molecular, to the animals and plants of the earth, and indeed to the very dust of which we are made, God has assumed all that in the Incarnation. For God's purpose, fighting against all the sources of our despair, from unemployment and oppression to the heat death of the universe, is to save the whole world.

> I consider that the sufferings of this present time are not worth comparing with the glory that is to be revealed to us. For the creation waits with eager longing for the revealing of the sons of God; for the creation was subjected to futility, not of its own will but by the will of him who subjected it in hope; because the creation itself will be set free from its bondage to decay and obtain the glorious liberty of the children of God. We know that the whole creation has been groaning in travail together until now; and not only the creation, but we ourselves, who have the first fruits of the Spirit, groan inwardly as we wait for adoption as sons, the redemption of our bodies. (Rom. 8:18-23)

(While reading this passage in his study, Luther is supposed to have turned to his dog and said, "You too shall have a little golden tail.")

The source of this new creation is Christ. Humanity "by itself" does not win control over nature, for we are part of nature. Cut off from Christ, the best humanity would be able to achieve would be an ability to manipulate the forces of nature which could magnify the evil which sin can accomplish. The human race does not "grow up" to lose its need of Christ. Instead, the true maturity of the human race comes *in* Christ (Eph. 4:13-16).

The scope of redemption is cosmic, for the redeemer is the one who created and who sustains the whole cosmos. God does not merely pluck a few souls out of a dying universe, but proclaims and shows his lordship over all that he has made. There will be new heavens and a new earth, and if there are intelligent extra-terrestrial beings, they somehow find their fulfillment in the Incarnation of the Word of God. And when the fulfillment of the world is complete, God's presence will shine forth from the body and the dwelling place which he has made for himself in the Incarnation, a body made transparent to the glory of God.

"O that deliverance for Israel would come out of Zion!" (Ps. 14:7).

The first book of the Bible speaks of the creation of the world. The last speaks not of the mere destruction of the world, but of its redemption and re-creation:

> And he who sat upon the throne said, "Behold, I make all things new." (Rev. 21:5a)

LEADER'S GUIDE

Introduction

The material here is designed to help the leaders of classes or discussion groups in which *The Trademark of God* is used as a major resource. There is a four-part structure for each chapter of the curriculum material. The following comments will indicate the purpose and possible uses for each part.

Notes contains a brief discussion of the fundamental issues and goals of the chapter. It is in the nature of the material that we're dealing with that there are a number of "side roads" which can be taken, and it is not always possible, or even desirable, to stick too single-mindedly to one narrow goal. However, the general purpose of the material should be kept in mind. The general cognitive, affective and "life-related" learning goals which have been kept in mind during the preparation of the material for this course are listed at the beginning of this leader's guide.

Matters Arising lists questions and comments which learners might bring up in discussing the chapter. These may involve matters about which there simply has not been time for adequate treatment, especially difficult or unfamiliar material, or matters about which there has been a considerable amount of debate and/or misinformation in our culture. The leader of a particular group will be, in general, in the best position to know the kind of

questions and comments that are likely to arise, and should be
prepared to deal with them in ways that will lead to helpful
discussion.

Openers provides material to start or help discussion. There
are some suggestions about types of current news items which
might provide a focus for discussion. If possible, such clippings
should be brought to the class. There are also questions which
might serve to start discussion. These are simply stated as
questions, in quotation marks. And there are some statements or
references to which some useful reaction from learners might be
expected. Again, the leader will be in the best position to know
what will best serve to stimulate discussion of the material.

Resources gives a few references for further study, or for
preparation by the leader. In most cases, these would be appropriate
for interested class members. (A few of the resources are marked
as "more advanced.") Books from these lists can probably be
obtained from a local public or college library, either directly or
through interlibrary loan, and many are still in print and can be
purchased.

Learning Goals for
The Trademark of God

COGNITIVE GOALS

To realize that "the redeemer is the creator."

To become acquainted with the organic and evolutionary character of God's universe.

To think about ways in which Christian faith and science can inform one another.

AFFECTIVE GOALS

To stand in awe of the scope of the lordship of Christ.

To appreciate the richness of the biblical witness concerning creation and redemption.

To have the courage to allow Christian faith and scientific understanding to inform one another.

LIFE-RELATED GOALS

To reflect on the roles of schools, families and churches in teaching about evolution and creation.

To connect our evolutionary understanding of creation with current concerns such as the environment, abortion, and men-women issues.

1. THE CREATOR OF EVOLUTION

Notes

The basic thing here is to present the issue associated with creation and evolution clearly, and to make clear the presuppositions of the course material. We also want to communicate an awareness of the controversial character of the subject. We are not interested in avoiding problems with some kind of "evolution in school, creation in church" approach, or in simply dismissing them by saying, "There's no problem—evolution is how God created."

The course involves some commitment to exploration. We're looking for possible answers to the question, "How can we develop and realize a Christian worldview which takes seriously the modern scientific picture of the world?"

Three fundamental presuppositions are made:

a. God is the creator of the entire universe. (Note—"is," not "was.")

b. The entire universe, and particularly life on earth, has evolved and is evolving. (While there will be some brief discussion of evidence for evolution, we will not really be concerned with *proving* evolution, any more than with *proving* creation.)

c. Christ the redeemer is the creator. (It is this which separates our work from those which overemphasize "reconciling Genesis and geology" and so forth.)

The first two of these presuppositions, taken together, make it clear that we are not at all concerned with "creation versus evolution."

The basic theme of "creation out of nothing" as "the trademark of God," a theme which will pervade the whole course, is introduced here.

Matters Arising

At this point, a number of basic issues which are "in the air"—the connection between evolution and atheism, fossil evidence for evolution, creation and evolution in public education, the reliability of Genesis—are likely to come up. Any extensive discussion of these topics probably needs to be delayed until they are dealt with in later chapters. It will be a good idea for the leader to make notes on questions and comments so that they really *can* be dealt with later.

Introducing Christ into a discussion of creation and evolution will be a surprise to many people. One reason why so many discussions of creation and evolution are unfruitful is because there is very little about them that is specifically *Christ*ian.

Openers

    a. There is likely to be current news about evolution in public education which can serve as a focus for discussion. (Newspaper articles and other such resources should be brought to class.)

    b. "How were creation and evolution discussed in your religious upbringing?"—or in the home or school?

    c. "What about evolution scares or comforts you?"

Resources

Eiseley, Loren. *The Firmament of Time.* New York: Atheneum, 1962.

Kopp, Joseph V. *Teilhard de Chardin / A New Synthesis of Evolution.* New York: Paulist, 1967.

Miller, Jonathan, and Van Loon, Borin. *Darwin for Beginners.* New York: Pantheon, 1982.

2. GOD'S TRADEMARK

Notes

This is basically a look at the theme of creation in the Old Testament. We start from what may appear to be an unusual point —not Genesis 1-3, but the Exodus and the Exile. That needs to be emphasized. It is done for two reasons. First, the thought of the Old Testament begins with God's saving work in history. (Note that, even if one adheres to the idea of Mosaic authorship of the Pentateuch, the Exodus would still predate the creation accounts of Genesis.) Secondly, starting in an unfamiliar place may keep us from thinking, "We know all this."

In content, the stress is on "the trademark of God"—God creates out of nothing. He raises the dead, justifies by grace, and gives hope to the hopeless. The statement of James A. Sanders about prophetic faith (*Torah and Canon* [Philadelphia: Fortress, 1972], p. 87) is relevant here:

> For the prophets were true monotheists, and nothing they said so stressed their monotheism as the idea that God was free enough of his chosen people to transform them in the crucible of destitution into a community whose members could themselves be free of every institution which in his providence he might give them. Their real hope, according to these prophets, lay in the God who had given them their existence in the first place, in his giving it to them again. Normal folk, in their right minds, know that hope is in having things turn out the way they think they should—by maintaining their view of life without let, threat, or hindrance. And normal folk believe in a god who will simply make things turn out that way. For them it is not a question of what God ought to do, that is clear: he will do what we know is right for him to do, if we simply trust and obey. Nobody in his right mind could possibly believe that God would want us to die in order to give us life again, or to take away the old institutions he first gave us in order to give us new ones.

This theme of "the trademark of God" carries through the whole course.

The *sea* / the Deep / chaos / monsters / is a powerful complex of symbols which is encountered throughout the Bible.

Matters Arising

   a. "Why are we starting here?" This has been discussed above. In addition to the comments there, we may also note that where we have chosen to start, in situations of despair and defeat, may hit closer to home than would "the beginning"— whether that was six thousand or ten billion years ago.

   b. Questions of biblical authorship could arise. "Mosaic authorship of the Pentateuch" isn't likely to be an issue, but our talk of "Second Isaiah" could raise questions. This is not central to our concern here. However, the force of the creation-redemption material in Isaiah 40-55 is greater if it is understood as coming *out of* the situation of exile and destruction rather than as something predicted long before.

Openers

   a. "Have you ever been in a hopeless situation and found hope?"

   b. "What kind of picture does 'creation out of nothing' call up for you?"

   c. Current "liberation theology" in Latin America places a strong emphasis on the Exodus. This could provide a focus for some discussion of the political and social relevance of the biblical doctrine of creation.

Resources

Hebert, Gabriel. *When Israel Came Out of Egypt.* Richmond, VA: John Knox Press, 1961.

Mays, James Luther. *Ezekiel, Second Isaiah* (*Proclamation Commentaries*). Philadelphia: Fortress, 1978.

Throckmorton, Burton H., Jr. *Creation by the Word.* Boston: United Church Press, 1968.

von Rad, Gerhard. *Old Testament Theology*, vols. 1 and 2. New York: Harper & Row, 1962. (More advanced)

3. "IN THE BEGINNING . . ."

Notes

Our major concern in this chapter is to study the theological emphases of the creation accounts of Genesis. Genesis 1:1-2:4a stresses the sovereignty of God in creation. The second account, Genesis 2:4b-25, is more interested in God's immediate concern for humanity. We have, then, two accounts which complement one another.

Since these stories are so familiar, it is important to try to make some effort to read them without assuming that we already know what they say. It would be good if learners could read the first two chapters of Genesis during the week before this class, trying to read them as if they had never encountered them before. (Of course we know that this is not entirely possible, but even making the effort may make it possible for some new things to be seen.)

Whether or not Genesis 1:1-3 teaches creation out of nothing in the strict philosophical sense, it is clear that the only "power" behind creation in the first account is God. He is in complete control. On the other hand, the creation of living things is mediated—the waters and earth bring them forth at God's command. Thus there is some continuity of thought with evolutionary theory. The ideas of Gregory of Nyssa suggest some of the creative possibilities of the Christian tradition in regard to Genesis 1 and 2.

Matters Arising

    a. Many questions which will arise ultimately relate to the question of the *types* of accounts present in Genesis 1-2. We do not insist on reading them as strict historical accounts, in the naive sense, in part because they don't invite us to read them in that way. This is seen, for one thing, from the fact that we have two different accounts whose "harmonization" is artificial.

    If we ask, then, "Are these creation accounts true in the light of what science has discovered about the origins of the universe and of life?" we have to pay attention to the types of accounts we're dealing with. The Genesis accounts will appear to be "wrong" only if they are treated as modern scientific reports. By the same token, modern scientific papers on the Big Bang or evolution are "wrong" if they are regarded as presenting theological statements about the ultimate causes of the universe or of life.

    b. What is the justification for separating the whole creation story into two accounts? The differences in style and emphasis are fairly clear just from a reading of the English versions. Of course differences in vocabulary come out more clearly in the original Hebrew. For example, the first account uses the Hebrew verbs for "create" and "make," while the second uses "model" and "build." The different divine names, *Elohim* (God) and *Yahweh Elohim* (Lord God) provide another example.

Openers

    a. "Close your eyes, clear your minds, and listen to Genesis 1:1-5. What are your responses?"

    b. "Do you remember Christmas Eve of 1968? What were your feelings and thoughts about Apollo 8 and Genesis?"

    c. "What does Genesis really say about Adam and Eve as individuals?"

d. There are sometimes newspaper articles about current issues in biblical interpretation. These might be brought to class, especially if they have some bearing on Genesis.

Resources

Bonhoeffer, Dietrich. *Creation and Fall* and *Temptation.* New York: Macmillan, 1959. (More advanced)

Gregory of Nyssa. "On the Making of Man," in vol. 5 of *The Nicene and Post-Nicene Fathers.* 2d ser. Grand Rapids, MI: Eerdmans, 1979. (More advanced)

Hyers, Conrad. *The Meaning of Creation: Genesis and Modern Science.* Atlanta: John Knox, 1984.

Thielicke, Helmut. *How the World Began.* Philadelphia: Fortress, 1961.

Westermann, Claus. *The Genesis Accounts of Creation.* Philadelphia: Fortress, 1964.

4. THE REDEEMER IS THE CREATOR

Notes

There are two fundamental themes here in dealing with re-creation in the New Testament. First, there is a strong Johannine emphasis on the idea that the creator of the world is present in Jesus. Then the Pauline idea of justification by grace through faith is seen to correspond to the concept of creation out of nothing. This comes out most clearly in Romans 4.

There are four things which we want to convey *affectively.*

a. The "mobility" of God—the temple is replaced by a person.
b. The cross and resurrection of Christ together are the clearest example of God's trademark.
c. The fundamental Reformation emphasis on justification is closely related to God's trademark.

d. Salvation is new creation.

The last part of the chapter prepares for a transition to discussion of scientific material for awhile. We suggest that Darwinian evolution via natural selection also bears God's trademark, and point out that God has given wisdom to human beings so that we can understand creation.

Matters Arising

a. There may be some confusion and questioning about the association of Christ with creation. The threefold split of Luther's Small Catechism, with Father and Creation, Son and Redemption, and Holy Spirit and Sanctification, contributes to that. A balance to that comes again from Luther in "A Mighty Fortress Is Our God," when he says of Christ, "There is no other God." But perhaps the best things to stress are John 1 and the Nicene Creed.

b. There may be some question about miracles and the way in which they relate to creation. The emphasis here, following St. Athanasius and C.S. Lewis (in *Miracles*), is on the idea that the miracles of Jesus show the presence of the creator.

c. There might be some discussion of the Sabbath rest and the idea of ongoing creation.

d. Here, as well as in other places, the Apocrypha is cited. Bibles with this included should be available. There might be a *little* discussion of the proper use of the Apocrypha.

Openers

a. "What is God doing new *today?*"

b. "What sort of thoughts about the works of Father, Son, and Holy Spirit did you get from your confirmation instruction?"

    c. "How do you feel about the suggestion that Darwinian
       evolution is 'the same kind of thing' as God's creation out
       of nothing?'" (Note that this will be discussed later in
       more detail.)

    d. For response: In Dorothy Sayers's series of plays *The Man
       Born to Be King*, there is a place where Jesus quotes, "And
       God looked at everything He had made, and behold! it was
       very good." The stage directions say that this is to be said
       "with the implication that this was part of his [Jesus's] own
       experience."

Resources

    Lewis, C.S. *Miracles*. New York: Macmillan, 1947, especially
chapters 14-16.

    Reumann, John. *Creation and New Creation*. Minneapolis:
Augsburg, 1973.

    Throckmorton, Burton H., Jr. *Creation by the Word*. Boston:
United Church Press, 1968.

5. "WHEN THE MORNING STARS SANG TOGETHER"

Notes

    When the whole universe is covered in a few pages, it's obvious
that there has to be a lot of condensation! There are two basic
goals of this survey, a cognitive one and an affective one. *Cognitively*,
the learner should get a rough idea of the way in which current
scientific theories picture the universe. In particular, we want to
convey the idea that the universe is not something static. Teilhard
de Chardin's idea of "cosmogenesis rather than cosmos" is
appropriate here. *Affectively*, we hope that there will be some awe
at the scope of God's creation in space and in time.

    The treatment of cosmology is very abbreviated. A simple

model of the universe (due to Milne), in which we picture the galaxies as fragments blown out from an explosion, is used. We do, however, point out the general limitations of models. The three basic, interrelated pieces of evidence mentioned are

 a. galactic redshifts, showing the expansion of the universe,
 b. discovery of the fireball radiation, and
 c. radioactive dating.

Describing a scale model of the galaxy may give a little feeling for the size of things. If a model were made with the sun an inch in diameter, the earth, with a diameter of about .01 inches, would be nine feet away from it, and the nearest star would be about 460 *miles* from the sun. The diameter of the galaxy on this scale would be about ten *million* miles.

Another model may help to establish the time perspective. If the Big Bang, taken as having occurred fifteen billion years ago, is taken as the beginning of a day and the present is at day's end, the earth would have been formed around five o'clock in the afternoon. At three minutes till midnight, the evolutionary tracks leading to present-day apes and humans had not yet separated. And all the history of the last ten thousand years would be squeezed into less than a tenth of a second before midnight.

Matters Arising

 a. Why do we need to be concerned with this? Our answer here is a theological one, based on what we studied in chapter 3. God created a good universe, and it's worth our effort to know about the world God created.
 b. There are a lot of things that people may have heard of, but which we simply haven't had time to do any justice to: steady-state cosmology, quasars, black holes, extraterrestrial life and the question of whether or not the universe will eventually collapse, to name a few. It will be useful for the leader to look at the resources enough at least to know what these terms refer to.

c. The topic of radioactive dating may bring to mind some doubts. Aren't there problems with radiocarbon dating? And how can we know what amounts of different atoms were present when the earth was formed? We are not making any use of radiocarbon dating (which is useful for time spans a good deal shorter than the age of the earth) here. And it is true that some assumptions about the initial abundances of elements have to be made. Some assumptions always underlie any scientific calculation. On the other hand, we simply cannot allow the claim sometimes made, that God could have created the universe a few thousand years ago, but arranged it to look billions of years old. That would amount to saying that God made a gigantic lie.

Openers

a. What is the reaction to the space and time scale models described under *Notes*?
b. "Is it proper to spend millions of dollars on space exploration, and especially on things like orbiting telescopes to learn the age of the universe, when there are so many problems on earth that we haven't dealt with?"
c. "We've said that 'human imagination is not content to stop short of the beginning.' Should it be?"

Resources

Crick, Francis. *Life Itself.* New York: Simon and Schuster, 1981.

Ferris, Timothy. *The Red Limit.* New York: Bantam, 1979.

Weinberg, Steven. *The First Three Minutes.* New York: Bantam, 1979.

6. DUST THAT DREAMS

Notes

We want to give here some understanding of, and feeling for, the revolutions brought about by the discoveries of the extinction and generation of species and the Darwinian theory of evolution. The discussions again must be very brief. We need to cover the theory of evolution as a whole, and then look at human evolution and the genetic basis for the whole thing.

We begin with the fact of extinction. Today nobody denies this, but two hundred years ago it was a serious problem for what then passed for theology. Eiseley's essay "How Death Became Natural" (in *The Firmament of Time*) is useful here. The fact of extinction, and especially the idea that evolution comes about through extinction, provides an excellent illustration of the way that the trademark of God is impressed upon the history of life.

It is important to convey the peculiarly *Darwinian* aspects of evolution, and to distinguish his theory from other evolutionary ideas. Both "evolution in general" and Darwinism are theologically significant. Any theory of evolution which links up humanity with other creatures enables us to connect the Incarnation with the entire history of life—as we will do in later chapters. Specifically Darwinian evolution, on the other hand, displays most clearly the "creation out of nothing" aspect of evolution.

Matters Arising

a. Of course there is a great deal of literature challenging evolution, both on scientific and on theological grounds. The purpose here has not been to prove evolution scientifically—there is simply not enough time. It should be realized, however, that most arguments against evolution have a theological basis. While the scientific community can, of course, be wrong, it is worth pointing out that supposedly scientific challenges to evolution (and not just to one or the other theory of the way evolution works) have not been taken very seriously by the scientific community for some time. A person should read the arguments on both sides with an open mind. In order to do that, it's necessary to suspend any idea that evolution contradicts Christianity.

b. There have been recent challenges to previously accepted models of evolution on scientific grounds. (For example, it is argued that evolution doesn't proceed at a uniform rate.) These are not challenges to evolution itself. There is often a temptation to a "God of the gaps" approach—if we don't understand how evolution happened, God must have been intervening. That's a risky approach, because further discoveries may remove the "need" for such a God.

c. On the other hand, it has to be admitted that our understanding of the initial stages of the formation of life—"chemical evolution"—is still pretty sketchy. (This is dealt with briefly at the end of chapter 5.)

d. Some learners may have encountered the ideas of Teilhard de Chardin. We'll make use of some of these in later chapters. While some of his ideas are very helpful, his view of evolution is not completely compatible with Darwinism, and consequently is somewhat different from the approach of this course.

Openers

a. "Why do you accept—or reject—evolution?"

b. "In one of the early debates on Darwin's theory, a bishop of the Anglican Church concluded his attack on evolution by sarcastically asking his opponent if he were descended from the ape on his grandmother's side or on his grandfather's. What would be your response to this?"

c. There will probably be current news items relating to evolution—e.g., fossil discoveries—which can be brought for discussion.

Resources

Eiseley, Loren. *The Firmament of Time.* New York: Atheneum, 1962.

Gould, Stephen Jay. *Ever Since Darwin.* New York: W.W. Norton & Co., 1977.

Leakey, Richard E., and Lewin, Roger. *Origins.* London: Macdonald and Jane's, 1977. (Especially for human evolution.)

Miller, Jonathan, and Van Loon, Borin. *Darwin for Beginners.* New York: Pantheon, 1982.

Morris, Henry M. *The Scientific Case for Creation.* San Diego: CLP Publishers, 1977. (This gives the "creationist" view.)

Teilhard de Chardin, Pierre. *The Phenomenon of Man.* New York: Harper & Row, 1959.

7. THE BATTLE OF THE CENTURY

Notes

This chapter surveys some of the areas of tension between evolutionary thought and Christian ideas regarding creation. Underlying the whole course is the presupposition that these can fit together harmoniously. However, there is no point in ignoring controversies and problems. The areas of debate may be grouped as follows.

1. Problems Christians have with evolution.
   a. Public education. (The treatment here is implicit, in that our decisions about how evolution and creation should be taught will depend on our answers to other questions.)
   b. Social Darwinism and Nazism. (This isn't "solved" here —we deal with it in chapter 11.)
   c. Biblical authority.
   d. The basis for morality.
   e. The question of purpose for life.
   f. The "scandal" of evolution.

2. Objections to the Christian doctrine of creation.
   a. Creationism.
   b. Ecological arguments.
   c. The "enslavement" of humanity (as, for example, argued by Marx).

This chapter really is bringing to a head some of the issues which could surface at other points during the course. The leader should use his or her discretion in deciding when discussion would be most fruitful.

Matters Arising

a. The education issue is certainly important, and will have to be dealt with. While several approaches may be taken, there are a couple of points to bear in mind. First, it is ultimately disastrous for children to be taught in school that evolution and Christianity have to be in conflict. Secondly, the idea that nothing *at all* can be said about religious ideas concerning creation in public schools is an extreme, though popular, interpretation of the establishment clause of the First Amendment.

b. It is quite likely that some learners will believe that they have no problem with evolution because they have not really seen the implications of the specifically *Darwinian* aspects of evolution.

c. Connections between Marxism-Leninism and evolution, briefly alluded to in the chapter, might be pursued further if there is interest. ("Lysenkoism," concerning which Martin Gardner has a chapter in *Fads and Fallacies in the Name of Science*, is an interesting aspect of this.)

Openers

a. "How should evolution and creation be presented in public schools? In church schools?"

b. "In what ways would it have been more comfortable to believe in special creation, as people could three hundred years ago, without worrying about evolution?"

c. "How does being related to the 'lower animals' affect your image of yourself?"

d. "What do you think is the basic reason that so many Christians have had problems with evolution?"

Resources

Gould, Stephen Jay. *Ever Since Darwin.* New York: W.W. Norton & Co., 1977.

Haeckel, Ernst. *The Riddle of the Universe.* London: Watts & Co., 1929. (This provides a good example of older evolution-based attacks on Christianity. Haeckel was one of the major evolutionary scientists of the nineteenth century.)

Loewenberg, Bert James. *Darwinism Comes to America, 1859-1900.* Philadelphia: Fortress, 1969.

The 1982 court decision concerning the Arkansas "Balanced Treatment for Creation-Science and Evolution-Science Act" was reprinted in *Science* of 19 February 1982.

8. A CHAPTER ABOUT NOTHING

Notes

This is an important chapter, and also a hard one. We don't have final answers about the origin of evil, and must be content to think about possibilities. Perhaps it should be emphasized that we don't *have* to understand why there is evil, though it is foolish to deny the seriousness of the problem that evil presents us with in our lives.

There are two parts to this:

a. The character of evil and sin as nothingness.

b. Speculations concerning the origin of evil in the world.

It's hard to talk about evil precisely because there's nothing to get hold of. Turning away from the creator (Romans 1) is the basic sin. (Note also the way in which Luther deals with the Commandments in his *Small Catechism*—the explanations of 2 through 10 tie them to 1.)

The possibilities for the origin of evil in creation are as follows:

a. The traditional "Fall" narrative.
b. An evolutionary picture with humanity "turning from the path to God" somewhere along the way. Since Romans connects death with sin, it's hard to see how the billions of years of death preceding the appearance of the human race are to be dealt with. One point we make is that a later event can change the *meaning* of the events preceding it, as with the example of the American Civil War.
c. Some connection of sin with the traditional Satan—with the "powers"—can help to give our picture of evil the appropriate cosmic scope. (But note that while one may believe that there is a personal devil, Christians don't "believe in the devil" in the same sense that they believe in Christ.)
d. Evil as the "shadow" of creation, following Teilhard. Here we have to avoid the error of thinking that there is some "evil god," independent of God.

Matters Arising

a. The distinction between sins and Sin may need to be discussed further. Romans 1 is the best resource for that.
b. What about the connection between the serpent of Genesis 3 and Satan? The development of this tradition may need to be explored somewhat further.
c. How can human sin have caused death? That is precisely one of the major puzzles. Discussions about the Civil War, things going backward in time in modern physics and so

forth aren't intended to provide final answers, but to show
possible ways of thinking about the problem.
d. "Is God the creator of evil?" is a question that will have
to be confronted, especially with the "shadow" of creation
idea.

Openers

a. "What do you think of when you hear the word *sin?*"
b. "Are there connections between the idea of evil as nothingness and such features of modern society as sexual perversion,
genocide, nuclear war, abortion, and *anorexia nervosa?*"
c. The question of evil is often best dealt with in fiction.
Solzhenitsyn's chapter on Stalin, "Old Age," in *The First
Circle* and Charles Williams's *Descent into Hell* provide good
examples.
d. "What would it have meant for God to create a universe
in which there was no *possibility* of evil?"
e. Reading the third and/or fourth oracles against Tyre
(Ez. 28:1-10 and/or 11-19) might be a good way of getting
into this topic.

Resources

Bonhoeffer, Dietrich. *Creation and Fall* and *Temptation*. New
York: Macmillan, 1959. (More advanced)
Florovsky, Georges. "The Darkness of Night," in *Creation
and Redemption*. Belmont, MA: Nordland, 1976. (More advanced)
Lewis, C.S. *The Problem of Pain*. New York: Macmillan, 1962.
Teilhard de Chardin, Pierre. "Fall, Redemption, and Geo-
centrism," "Notes on Some Possible Historical Representations
of Original Sin," and "Reflections on Original Sin," in *Christianity
and Evolution*. New York: Harcourt Brace Jovanovich, 1971.
Williams, Charles. *Descent into Hell*. Grand Rapids, MI:
Eerdman's, 1965.

9. WHAT HAS NOT BEEN ASSUMED HAS NOT BEEN REDEEMED

Notes

Our concern here is with the doctrine of the Incarnation and the ways in which it can connect up with evolutionary thought. There has already been some coverage of this material in chapter 4. This repetition is appropriate, since the topic is central to the whole course. The following themes can be distinguished.

a. The birth, life, death, and resurrection of Jesus show God's presence and trademark.

b. The thrust of the two-natures doctrine is, "*God* saves the *whole* human being."

c. It is "human nature in general" or "unpersonal" (as distinguished from "impersonal" in the usual sense) human nature which is assumed in the Incarnation. This is very important for the idea of the salvation of all creation and the "theological proof of evolution."

d. The "theological proof of evolution"—combining the basic principle that "what has not been assumed has not been redeemed" and the biblical witness that the whole creation is to be redeemed allows us to show *theologically* that evolution is superior to "special creation."

We have not concentrated here on biblical texts which support the two-natures doctrine. It would, however, be a good idea for the leader to have some of the appropriate texts available (for example John 1:1-3, 14, 20:27-28; Galatians 4:4; Hebrews 1:3, 2:17).

Matters Arising

a. There may be some questions about the doctrine of the virginal conception—evidence, reasons, and significance.

b. The idea of the unpersonal human nature of Christ will be puzzling because unfamiliar. The following points may be made.

1. We aren't dealing with "personality" in the modern sense.
2. The point is not that there is no person in Christ, but that the unpersonal *human* nature is enpersoned (from the first instant of conception) in the person of the Word. Jesus always has the personal centering constituted by his total commitment to the Father.
3. This does not mean any denial of Jesus's full humanity.
4. This doctrine is necessary in order to avoid the idea of "two persons," and thus "two sons."

c. The idea of the salvation of all creation ("dog heaven") will probably evoke some discussion. We aren't talking about naive universalism here—it is possible for individuals to turn away from God forever. As far as the salvation of other animals is concerned, Lewis's chapter on "Animal Pain" in *The Problem of Pain* is good.

Openers

a. "How do you picture Jesus?" (Pictures showing Jesus as black, oriental, etc. may help to illustrate the idea of "general human nature." For that matter, note that those are as accurate historically as our familiar pictures showing him as a blond Caucasian!)
b. "Does Jesus understand computers?" (This seems like a dumb question. What is wanted is a snap response. The point is that we have a tendency to picture Jesus, in spite of the fact that he *is* God Incarnate, merely as a first-century Jew, rather old-fashioned in comparison with *our* sophistication.)
c. "One antievolution book argues that evolution is un-Christian because it makes Jesus into just a special made-over ape. What is your feeling about that?"
d. A study of the way in which Matthew 2:15 uses Hosea 11:1 and Exodus 4:22 can provide another useful example of Jesus's "recapitulation" of the history of God's people.

Resources

Athanasius. "On the Incarnation of the Word," in *Christology of the Later Fathers*, ed. Edward R. Hardy. Philadelphia: Westminster, 1954. (More advanced)

Knutson, Kent S. *His Only Son Our Lord.* Minneapolis: Augsburg, 1966.

Lewis, C.S. *The Problem of Pain.* New York: Macmillan, 1962, especially chapter 9, "Animal Pain."

Robinson, H. Wheeler. *Corporate Personality in Ancient Israel.* Philadelphia: Fortress, 1980.

10. "THE DUST OF DEATH"

Notes

It is important to make connections between this chapter and the previous one. The cross and resurrection are intimately connected with one another, and the combination cannot be extracted from the Incarnation without destroying the point of the whole thing. There are several things that we want to convey here.

a. Proper theology is "theology of the cross"—God reveals himself in weakness and suffering.

b. The emphasis is on Good Friday plus Easter *as a whole.* The Lord of Glory "rode the black horns of the cross" (Campbell), and the crucified one is the risen Lord.

c. This complex of events has the character which we have come to expect of God's creative work.

d. The affective goal is not a twofold "Poor Jesus/Whew, it's okay after all" one. Rather, one appropriate response (though not the only one) is awe and marvel at the audacity of the plunge which God takes.

e. Resurrection is not mere reversal, but glorification and establishment of Jesus with the immediate rule of the universe.

Matters Arising

    a. "How can God die?" We could talk about that somewhat theoretically in terms of the communication of attributes in the personal union of human and divine. But the rock-bottom answer, whether we understand the "how" or not, is, "He suffered under Pontius Pilate, was crucified, died, and was buried," as we confess in the Apostles' Creed.

    b. Questions about whether or not God can suffer, whether or not Jesus was ignorant of some things according to his human nature, etc., may arise.

    c. What do we mean by resurrection? It is resurrection of the *body*. It is necessary to be quite clear about this. Whatever position one takes on "immortality of the soul," that issue is not central to Christian doctrine. In the creeds, we confess resurrection.

    d. How is Christ's resurrection related to ours? 1 Corinthians 15 may be studied profitably in this connection.

Openers

    a. "Does Easter change the evening news?"

    b. "Considering what crucifixion really was like, what are we doing when we receive the sign of the cross in benediction?"

    c. "What is your favorite holiday of the church year—Christmas, Good Friday, Easter, or Pentecost?"

    d. There might be some current news (about, e.g., the Shroud of Turin) which could be brought to class. This could serve to develop discussion about the historical character of the resurrection.

Resources

Brown, Raymond E. *The Virginal Conception and Bodily Resurrection of Jesus.* New York: Paulist, 1973.

Hengel, Martin. *Crucifixion.* Philadelphia: Fortress, 1977. (More advanced)

Knutson, Kent S. *His Only Son Our Lord.* Minneapolis: Augsburg, 1966.

Prenter, Regin. *Luther's Theology of the Cross.* Philadelphia: Fortress, 1971.

Ramsey, A.M. *The Resurrection of Christ.* 2d ed. London: Bles, 1946.

11. EVOLUTIONARY ETHICS

Notes

The intent in this section is not so much to develop an evolutionary ethic from the ground up as to look at some of the connections between an evolutionary view of the world and ethical concerns *in the light of the gospel.* There are two types of questions to deal with.

a. In what ways, and in what areas, is it necessary for us to transcend old patterns of behavior? Are there patterns which had at least some limited survival value in the past, but which are no longer helpful at our present stage of biological and cultural development?

b. In what positive ways can an evolutionary understanding aid and motivate our ethical responses?

"Tribal" (including racial and national) separation and gender subordination are examples of evolutionary strategies of the past which have outlived their usefulness, whatever that may have been in the past. They are not in accord with the Christian vision that is to motivate our behavior. Thus they are in the "You have heard that it was said to the people long ago . . . but I tell you . . ." category (cf. Mt. 5:21-22, NIV).

On the other hand, evolutionary understanding underscores and reinforces the idea of our unity with the rest of creation. Abortion and environmental issues are examples of those where such an understanding is helpful.

A fundamental assumption here is that our behavior is to be informed by our realization that God has become human.

Matters Arising

a. It is hard to guess what could catch fire here. Discussions of racism and sexism have the potential for initiating a considerable amount of discussion. The point made here is that an understanding of how we got here is important, but that it doesn't necessarily give us directions about how to move forward.

b. Were war and oppression *right* in the past, though wrong now? No, but we can only see that clearly in the light of Christ. The Incarnation and cross give meaning to events coming before as well as after them.

c. What about the "orders of creation"? An idea of static "orders" doesn't fit in very well with an evolutionary view. Nor is the idea of orders of creation a strongly biblical one.

d. Can the "animal rights" idea really be taken seriously? As we have said, this topic may serve best just to sharpen awareness.

Openers

a. Genetic engineering—interferon, plant hybrids, human gene manipulation, etc.—is very much in the news. This is a very direct way in which we influence evolution. It can be a very provocative discussion topic. E.g., especially with modification of human genetics, "Who will be in charge?" ("Who will guard the guardians?")

b. Is it *safe* for human beings to be able to influence the direction of their own biological change?

c. "What kind of responsibility do we have toward other species? Is there any ethical difference between eating meat and doing laboratory experiments on animals?"

d. "Is competition Christian?"

e. "We've said that racism and sexism aren't in accord with
the gospel, while a sense of unity with the environment is.
Why has it been that Christian cultures have continued with
racism and sexism while they haven't shown a lot of concern
for the environment?"

Resources

Gould, Stephen Jay. *Ever Since Darwin.* New York: W.W.
Norton & Co., 1977.

Leakey, Richard E., and Lewin, Roger. *Origins.* London:
Macdonald and Jane's, 1977.

Lewis, C.S. *The Abolition of Man.* New York: Macmillan,
1947.

Reed, Evelyn. *Woman's Evolution.* New York: Pathfinder
Books, 1975. (A rather different view from that of, e.g., Leakey
and Lewin. More advanced.)

12. "UNTO THE AGES OF AGES"

Notes

This chapter is in the form of a major question and responses
to it. "Where is evolution going?" In a purely secular way, we
can answer that human beings, through cooperation and technology, have achieved some control of their own evolution.
Theologically—or, in Teilhardian terms, looking at the "within"
of things—it is the church as the "body of Christ" which is the
true "nucleation center" of the new creation. Evolution becomes
convergence on Christ. The Pauline idea of the body of Christ,
influenced by Teilhard, is strong here.

Again, we are talking about *cosmic* salvation—about re-creation.
The idea that dogs and cats and dinosaurs are saved is sensible only

with a proper emphasis on the resurrection of their *context*. (Lewis's chapter "Animal Pain," referred to earlier, should be noted.)

Some pains should be taken to avoid an overly optimistic progressivism which ignores sin. Evil is not yet abolished, and autonomous humanity in charge of its own evolution leads to disaster. *The Abolition of Man* can serve as a useful conservative corrective to the idea of "humanity's conquest of nature."

In the life of the church, the Eucharist makes close contact with the theme of this chapter. It might be helpful to look at some of the eschatological emphases of the liturgy—e.g., "Give us a foretaste of the feast to come." Teilhard's "The Mass on the World" is a good example of relevant piety in the Roman Catholic tradition.

Matters Arising

a. There may be some discussion of future directions of evolution which will take a science fiction turn.

b. What about extraterrestrials or artificial intelligence? We have not had time to do more than mention the first of these in passing. How to deal with them in light of the principle that "What has not been assumed has not been redeemed" is not completely clear.

c. Again, we are not talking about a naive universalism. All natures, all "types," are redeemed, but there is still the possibility for individuals to turn away from God. Hell still exists, at least as a logical possibility, but, in the end, it is no longer any threat to God's work.

d. We usually think of the risen Christ as the one seated at the right hand of the Father. What is the connection between the risen Lord and the Church as the Body of Christ? Christ is the *head* of his body, which is the church. Because the omnipresence of God is communicated to the humanity of Christ in the personal union of the Incarnation, Christ is present with his church on earth according to his humanity. There are several senses of the phrase "Body of Christ"

which can be distinguished. Robinson's *The Body* is helpful
for the Pauline concept.

Openers

    a. "What do you think of when you pray, 'Your kingdom
come'?"
    b. "How does it make you feel to think of yourself as an 'organ'
of the Body of Christ?"
    c. "Would you be disappointed if we were to find that earth
is the only planet in the galaxy with life?"

Resources

Lewis, C.S. *The Abolition of Man.* New York: Macmillan,
1947.

Robinson, John A.T. *The Body.* Philadelphia: Westminster,
1952. (More advanced)

Teilhard de Chardin, Pierre. *Christianity and Evolution.* New
York: Harcourt Brace Jovanovich, 1971.

Teilhard de Chardin, Pierre. "The Mass on the World," in
Hymn of the Universe. New York: Harper & Row, 1965.

AN ANNOTATED BIBLIOGRAPHY ON
CREATION, EVOLUTION, AND CHRISTOLOGY

It would be impossible to give a complete bibliography on even one of these topics in this limited space. The following lists do not pretend to be comprehensive, but only provide suggestions for those who may want to explore some of the relevant material more thoroughly. Though there is some overlap with the resources suggested in the leader's guide material, the references here are intended to complement those lists.

A number of the books listed here assume some technical background in one or more of the sciences or in theology. Some will also provide further bibliographies for more extended work.

References have been listed alphabetically under the headings *Cosmology and Cosmogony, Evolution, Theological Background, Evolution and Theology,* and *Education.* Brief comments are included on each listing.

COSMOLOGY AND COSMOGONY

Barrow, John D. and Silk, Joseph. *The Left Hand of Creation.* New York: Basic Books, 1983.

A nontechnical account of some of the most recent

129

scientific theories of the universe, including such ideas as the "inflationary" universe.

Berendzen, Richard; Hart, Richard; and Seeley, Daniel. *Man Discovers the Galaxies.* New York: Science History Publications, 1976.

　　A historical treatment of the observational discoveries of early modern cosmology. There is some emphasis on the personalities involved.

Dermott, S.F., ed. *The Origin of the Solar System.* New York: John Wiley & Sons, 1978.

　　This contains general surveys of our understanding, as well as papers directed toward specific aspects of the problem of the origin of the solar system.

Goldsmith, Donald and Owen, Tobias C. *The Search for Life in the Universe.* Menlo Park, CA: Benjamin/Cummings, 1980. With a foreword by Carl Sagan.

　　A definite discovery of extraterrestrial life would pose some interesting theological questions. This book surveys the status of searches for life beyond the earth.

Munitz, Milton K., ed. *Theories of the Universe.* New York: The Free Press, 1957.

　　A collection of original sources, with some commentary, from ancient times through the cosmologies of general relativity, kinematic relativity, and the steady-state theory. The more modern selections, while by experts, are not highly technical.

North, J.D. *The Measure of the Universe.* Oxford, England: Oxford University Press, 1965.

　　This provides extensive history and analysis of scientific cosmology, allowing the reader to understand the developments preceding the important discoveries which began in the 1960s. There is also a fair discussion of some of the philosophical issues.

Peebles, P.J.E. *Physical Cosmology.* Princeton, NJ: Princeton University Press, 1971.

Implications of observational data for cosmological theory are discussed here in a fairly technical fashion.

Raychaudhuri, A.K. *Theoretical Cosmology.* Oxford, England: Clarendon Press, 1979.

This gives a technical survey of the viable modern cosmological theories.

Sagan, Carl, and Shklovskii, I.S. *Intelligent Life in the Universe.* San Francisco: Holden-Day, 1966.

In this intriguing collaboration, the whole range of topics bearing on the problem of extraterrestrial intelligence is surveyed. A good deal of the material is pertinent to the issue of the origin of life on earth. Because of progress in space exploration, some of the material is now dated.

EVOLUTION

Ayala, Francisco J., and Valentine, James W. *Evolving: The Theory and Processes of Organic Evolution.* Menlo Park, CA: Benjamin-Cummings, 1979.

A text introducing the basic ideas of modern evolutionary theory.

Crick, Francis. *Life Itself.* New York: Simon and Schuster, 1981.

Fundamental issues concerned with the problem of the origin of life, together with more speculative ideas about "directed panspermia," are treated by one of the co-discoverers of the structure of DNA.

Darwin, Charles. *On the Origin of Species.* London: J.W. Dent & Sons, 1972.

Of course this is *the* classic on Darwinian evolution. It exists in many other editions and printings.

Dobzhansky, Theodosius. *Genetics of the Evolutionary Process.* New York: Columbia University Press, 1971.

The title of this work by one of the century's leading geneticists is self-explanatory.

Gillispie, Charles Coulston. *Genesis and Geology.* New York: Harper & Row, 1959.

    The subtitle summarizes the content: "A study in the relations of scientific thought, natural theology, and social opinion in Great Britain, 1790-1850."

Gould, Stephen Jay. *Ever Since Darwin.* New York: W.W. Norton & Co., 1977.

    A collection of readable and provocative essays on various aspects of evolution.

Klotz, John W. *Genes, Genesis, and Evolution.* St. Louis: Concordia Publishing House, 1955.

    Though written before the present period of evolution-creationism debates, this conservative Lutheran argument against evolution is still instructive. The tone is more calm than that of many such works.

Kofahl, Robert E. *Handy Dandy Evolution Refuter.* San Diego: Beta Books, 1980.

    This provides a useful compendium of creationist arguments against evolution.

Leakey, Richard E., and Lewin, Roger. *Origins.* London: Macdonald and Janes, 1977.

    A very helpful survey, with a considerable number of diagrams and pictures, of our current understanding of human evolution. (There is a paperback edition by Dutton which does not contain the diagrams and pictures.)

Lovejoy, Arthur O. *The Great Chain of Being.* Cambridge, MA: Harvard University Press, 1964.

    These lectures, originally given in 1932-1933, give an understanding of the picture of nature which evolutionary theory had to develop in and against.

Reed, Evelyn. *Woman's Evolution.* New York: Pathfinder Books, 1975.

    "From matriarchal clan to patriarchal family"—this feminist treatment deals with the evolution of gender roles and related matters in ways quite different from those of, e.g., Leakey and Lewin.

Smith, John Maynard, ed. *Evolution Now.* San Francisco: Freeman, 1982.

This volume commemorating the centenary of Darwin's death presents a number of articles from *Nature* on current research topics.

Stokes, William Lee. *Essentials of Earth History.* 4th ed. Englewood Cliffs, NJ: Prentice-Hall, 1982.

This introductory text supplies the basic geological understanding needed for evolutionary theory.

THEOLOGICAL BACKGROUND

Bonhoeffer, Dietrich. *Creation and Fall* and *Temptation.* Translated by John C. Fletcher and Kathleen Downham. New York: Macmillan, 1959.

The first of these studies treats the Genesis creation accounts and brings them into contact with the christological center.

Chemnitz, Martin. *The Two Natures in Christ.* Translated by J.A.O. Preus. St. Louis: Concordia Publishing House, 1971.

This is the classic sixteenth-century work of Lutheran christology.

Hardy, Edward Rochie, with Richardson, Cyril C., ed. *Christology of the Later Fathers.* Volume 3 of the *Library of Christian Classics.* Philadelphia: Westminster, 1977.

A collection of some of the basic patristic material, including Athanasius's *On the Incarnation of the Word* and the decree of the Council of Chalcedon.

Pannenberg, Wolfhart. *Jesus—God and Man,* 2d ed. Translated by Lewis L. Wilkins and Duane A. Priebe. Philadelphia: Westminster, 1977.

A major attempt to understand christology "from below," studying and criticizing the christological tradition in the light of modern thought and understanding of Scripture.

Robinson, H. Wheeler. *Corporate Personality in Ancient Israel.* Philadelphia: Fortress, 1980.

> These two essays introduce a theme which is important for the tying together of christology and evolution.

Robinson, John A.T. *The Body.* Philadelphia: Westminster, 1952.

> A study of the background and meaning of the Pauline "Body of Christ" concept.

von Rad, Gerhard. *Old Testament Theology.* 2 volumes. Translated by D.M.G. Stalker. New York: Harper & Row, 1962 (vol. I) and 1965 (vol. II).

> Israel's understanding of creation and redemption are set within the whole theological understanding of the Old Testament.

Evolution and Theology

Abbott, Lyman. *The Theology of an Evolutionist.* Boston and New York: Houghton, Mifflin & Co., 1897.

> Evolution is presented here as part of the older liberal theology.

Benz, Ernst. *Evolution and Christian Hope.* Translated by Heinz G. Frank. Garden City, NY: Doubleday & Co., 1966.

> Benz deals with "man's concept of the future from the early fathers to Teilhard de Chardin." Teilhard is dealt with appreciatively, but also with some strong criticism. The book provides a useful orientation.

Birch, L. Charles. *Nature and God.* London: SCM Press Ltd., 1965.

> In this book a biologist presents a view of creation and evolution which is closely related to the modern approach of process theology.

Gregory of Nyssa. *Dogmatic Treatises, etc.* Volume 5 of *A Select Library of Nicene and Post-Nicene Fathers of the Christian Church,* 2d ser. Edited by Philip Schaff and Henry Wace. Reprint, Grand Rapids, MI: Eerdmans, 1976.

> Especially important for our topic is the treatise "On the Making of Man" (pp. 387-425).

MacKay, Donald. *The Clockwork Image*. London: Inter-Varsity Press, 1974.

Though not explicitly concerned with evolution, this is helpful in discussing how one can develop a holistic Christian view of human beings that takes into account the modern scientific understanding of the human "machinery."

Maloney, George A. *The Cosmic Christ from Paul to Teilhard*. New York: Sheed and Ward, 1968.

The emphasis here is on the cosmic dimension of christology. In some ways the book can be regarded as a Roman Catholic counterpart of Benz's. There is a helpful appendix, "Selected Quotations from the Greek Fathers."

Messenger, Ernest C. *Evolution and Theology*. New York: Macmillan, 1932.

Messenger attempts here to go as far as possible toward accepting evolution while still remaining within the boundaries set for Roman Catholic theologians in the early part of the century. The thorough study of patristic and medieval writers, and especially of Gregory of Nyssa, is very valuable.

Moore, James R. *The Post-Darwinian Controversies: A Study of the Protestant Struggle to Come to Terms with Darwin in Great Britain and America, 1870-1900*. New York: Cambridge University Press, 1979.

The title is self-explanatory.

Peacocke, A.R. *Science and the Christian Experiment*. London: Oxford University Press, 1971.

Evolution is viewed within the context of the total enterprise of understanding the coherence of scientific and theological approaches to reality.

Teilhard de Chardin, Pierre. *Christianity and Evolution*. Translated by René Hague. New York and London: Harcourt Brace Jovanovich, 1969.

_____. *Hymn of the Universe*. Translated by Gerald Vann. New York: Harper & Row, 1969.

_____. *The Phenomenon of Man*. Translated by Bernard Wall. New York: Harper & Row, 1959.

While other writings of Teilhard could be recommended, these three books provide a good survey of his thought. The general emphases are, respectively, on evolution and theology, "cosmic spirituality" and evolution.

EDUCATION

Apps, Jerold W. *How to Improve Adult Education in Your Church.* Minneapolis: Augsburg, 1972.

This provides a brief survey of theory and an emphasis on the practical aspects of adult education programs for churches. Chapter 10, "Discussing Controversial Issues," is pertinent here.

Knowles, Malcolm S. *The Modern Practice of Adult Education, from Pedagogy to Andragogy.* Revised and updated edition. Chicago: Follett Publishing Co., 1980.

An extensive treatment of the theory and practice of adult education in general.

McKenzie, Leon. *Adult Religious Education—The 20th Century Challenge.* West Mystic, CT: Twenty-Third Publications, 1975.

Theoretical and practical aspects of adult religious education are treated, with an emphasis on the latter. Criticisms of existing practice are helpful. The material on setting-up and evaluating adult programs is well presented.

INDEX

abortion, 7, 28, 87, 119, 125
Adam, 3, 20, 21, 57, 61, 87
angels, angelic powers, 62, 81
apartheid, 28
Apollo 8, 16, 107
Aristotle, 61, 91
Athanasius, xi, 61, 109

Barth, Karl, 87
Big Bang, 1, 32, 35, 53, 78, 107
Body of Christ, 4, 88, 93, 94, 126-128
Book of Nature, 5

chiasmic cosmology, xi
Christ, xi, 7, 27-29, 31, 37, 56,
    65, 67-70, 75-79, 84-89,
    93-96, 102, 103, 108, 109,
    118, 120, 121, 125
Civil War, 51, 61, 118
Copernicus, ix, xii
creationism, 4, 50, 116
creationists, 51, 54
creation out of nothing, 5, 14, 15,
    17, 27, 29-31, 41, 50, 59, 71,
    75, 76, 102, 105, 106, 108,
    110, 113
cross, 7, 15, 27, 28, 54, 64, 67, 72,
    75-78, 95, 108, 122, 123, 125

Darrow, Clarence, 49
Darwin, ix, 3, 31, 43-46
Darwinian . . . , x, 53, 109, 110,
    113, 116
"Darwin's Mistake," 52
Darwin's theory, 53
Deep, 9, 18, 31, 59, 64, 75, 76,
    105
Doppler effect, 34
dust, 21, 22, 38, 47, 51, 75, 78, 79,
    95

Einstein, ix, 92
embryo, 45, 67, 70
embryological, 45
Eucharist, 88, 94, 127
exile, 7, 11, 13, 14, 24, 25, 65, 73,
    104
exiles, 11, 13, 18, 74
Exodus, 7-11, 14, 24, 65, 73, 104,
    105
extinct, 41, 75, 81
extinction, 5, 31, 44, 46, 74, 76,
    83, 89, 113

fireball, 35-37, 111
flood, 14, 24
fossil, 1, 22, 41, 42, 44, 45, 103, 114

Galileo, 33
genetic code, 32, 47, 71
genetic engineering, 90, 125
genetic information, 47, 83
God Incarnate, xi, 65, 67, 68, 70,
    75, 87, 121
grace alone, 29
Gregory of Nyssa. 22, 23, 106

hell, 57, 73
Hitler, 57
Hubble, Edwin, 33–35

image of God, 19, 21, 22, 45, 54, 81
Incarnation, ix, 64, 66, 68, 71, 77,
    82, 85, 87, 89, 93, 95, 96, 113,
    120, 122, 125, 127

Jesus, 4, 7, 26–28, 48, 62, 64–70,
    75, 78, 79, 82, 85, 121, 122
Jesus Christ, 4, 7, 25, 54, 65–69

laws of nature, 3, 4, 26, 36, 37
Leavitt, Henrietta, 34
Lemaître, Georges, 36
Leopold-Loeb murder case, 49
Lewis, C.S., 63, 109, 121, 127
Luther, Martin, xi, 29, 77, 95, 109

Marx, 55, 116
Marxism-Leninism, 116
Marxist ideology, 50
Mendel, Gregor, 46

natural selection, 31, 43, 47
Nazi, 50, 83, 92
neo-Darwinian, x

new creation, 29, 31, 87, 96
Nicene Creed, 1, 65, 109

Omega Point, 89
Origin of Species, 3, 43

Pascal, Blaise, 1

racial segregation, 83
radioactive, 39, 111, 112
recapitulation, 69, 121
redshift, 35, 111
resurrection, 15, 27, 29, 30, 73
    76–80, 108, 122

sabbath, 20, 25, 28, 109
Satan, 62, 70, 118
Scopes "monkey trial," 49
Second Isaiah, 11
sickle-cell anemia, 44
Social Darwinism, 50, 115
Stalin, 57, 119
subordination of women, 84
"survival of the fittest," 31, 43, 50,
    86

Teilhard de Chardin, xi, xii, 63, 89,
    91, 110, 114, 118, 126, 127
Teilhardian, 126
Terence, 69
theology of the cross, xi, 122
trademark, 5, 14, 15, 24, 25, 30,
    50, 66, 71, 72, 102, 104, 120

Word, xi, 14, 18, 24, 37, 61
Word of God, ix, 5, 17, 19, 47, 60,
    69, 71, 87, 96